SPECIAL PRAISE FOR *PROCES*

"Dr. Jamie Marich's new book is a great introductio[illegible] as a way of treating trauma. Full of practical and accessible experiences, this is a wonderful gateway to reclaiming your creative soul while also being mindful of past traumas and moving forward in a gentle way. I highly recommend *Process Not Perfection* to anyone who desires to explore how creative process might help them along the road to emotional healing. With chapters exploring mindfulness, grounding, breath, compassion, your own edges, as well as others, this book encourages daily practice of play and presence."

—**Christine Valters Paintner,** PhD, Co-author of *Awakening the Creative Spirit: Bringing Expressive Arts to Spiritual Direction* and *The Wisdom of the Body: A Contemplative Journey to Wholeness for Women*

"As more and more forms of therapy come into public consciousness, we are, as a society, at long last learning new ways to heal. That makes *Process Not Perfection: Expressive Arts Solutions for Trauma Recovery* such important reading. It's filled with lesser known but extremely important forms of therapeutic expression and comes complete with exercises, recommendations, summaries and ideas for everyone—from the therapy newbie to the person who's tried everything.

—**Anna David**, New York Times Best Selling Author of *Party Girl*

"Dr. Marich has managed to capture what other books have not—a practical guide for those who want a heart-felt, embodied approach to self-care and healing. In this highly readable volume, the author clearly and passionately explains the many ways expressive methods can help each of us to once again feel not only whole, but also alive in our own bodies. Trauma is healed only through our commitment to an inner journey of reparation. This book will support you in that journey and give you countless dynamic approaches to support your transformation of mind, body and spirit."

—**Cathy Malchiodi,** PhD, LPCC, LPAT, ATR-BC, REAT, Director, Trauma Informed Practices and Expressive Arts Therapy Institute, Louisville, KY USA

"Every line in this book shows Jamie's authenticity, her love of the human spirit, and the fact that she is a cheerleader for all of us to find our way back to the home that has always been inside of us. Thank you for showing us how to use the expressive arts as a tangible, concrete, safe, and step-by-step process back into the body. A great book for those in healing as well as healers from all backgrounds looking for new and creative ways to be of service."

—**Kamini Desai,** PhD, Author of *Yoga Nidra: The Art of Transformational Sleep* Education Director, Amrit Yoga Institute

"Dr. Jamie Marich, my good friend and colleague, has a hashtag: #redefinetherapy. This is not just social media flash, it is a real goal, and Jamie is one of the premiere leaders in meeting that goal. *With Process Not Perfection*, Dr. Marich completes a journey that began with EMDR Therapy, moved into *Dancing Mindfulness*, and now expands into all of the Expressive Arts. Creativity as resourcing, creativity as healing, creativity as a healthy lifestyle are all made available here, not just for clinicians, but for everyone. This book is a turning point in the evolution of psychotherapy, a truly redefined picture of how we can heal and then remain in creativity and joy in the days to come."

—**Stephen Dansiger**, Psy.D., LMFT, Author of *Mindfulness for Anger Management*, *Clinical Dharma*, and *EMDR Therapy & Mindfulness for Trauma-Focused Care* (with Dr. Jamie Marich)

"Dr. Marich's language is gentle and inclusive yet direct and motivating and has a way of meeting the reader right where they are and encouraging them to take the next step in their process. The analogies in this book not only beautifully articulate what many of us who have suffered trauma intrinsically know to be true but they are sure to give even the most seasoned trauma experts new ways to help their clients understand the healing journey. As someone who used my craft as a performing artist as well as writing, yoga and mindfulness to help me in healing Complex-Post Traumatic Stress Disorder, I know firsthand how valuable those tools are and this book makes those tools and more accessible for every person who has been traumatized."

—**Marissa Ghavami**, Actor, Singer, Voice Over Artist, Model, Writer, Producer, Public Speaker and Founder of Healing TREE (Trauma Resources, Education & Empowerment)

"Gentle and encouraging, this book guides the reader to consider each channel of sensory, emotional, and cognitive awareness and how, when opened and welcomed, they can lead to expansiveness, expressiveness and, ultimately, to growth and healing. Less recipe than guidebook, Dr. Marich offers guidance and suggestions suitable for both the most tentative participant and the most engaged. Yes, it tells us, you exist in a complex, multi-layered way. *Yes*, you are allowed (even encouraged) to consider and explore those dimensions. The reader is shown how to cultivate curiosity about how it might look or sound or feel to become aware and to explore inner sensation, emotion, motion, and meaning. Yes, this might be scary to consider, but Dr. Marich illustrates with examples of processes others have undertaken. We all contain multitudes. And yes, there is meaning, growth and healing in their exploration and expression."

—**Dr. Mara Tesler Stein,** Co-Author of *Intensive Parenting: Surviving Your Emotional Journey Through the NICU;* Faculty Member, The Institute for Creative Mindfulness

"Written by a gifted trauma clinician, trainer, dancer, yogini, musician and educator, Jamie Marich weaves together her many decades of experience in the field of trauma recovery and the expressive arts. She has created a beautiful, informative and gentle phase-oriented guide for anyone with a history of trauma. While humans have been dancing, drumming, mark-making, singing and expressing their joy and suffering for centuries, this book weaves contemporary trauma theory with the expressive arts, an important contribution to our field. It will serve both as adjunct to anyone in trauma therapy, and as a scaffolding for people simply wishing to dip their toes into mindful healing practices that bring joy, expand 'window of tolerance', learn 'distress tolerance' techniques, and support their recovery through expression in many forms. Highly recommended to both laypersons and clinicians.

—**Carol McBride**, M.A., M.Ed., Creative Director, *The Trauma Project*

"*Process Not Perfection* is an inspiring and informative guide for anyone who wants to heal from trauma through the expressive arts. As a trauma specialist, Jamie Marich invites engagement with our own creative power to self-heal through directives that are easy to execute at home, using simple materials. The abundance of innovative expressive arts explorations in this book invite mind, heart, and body into deep and lasting healing."

—**Shelley Klammer**, MTC, RCS, REACE www.expressiveartworkshops.com

"As both a survivor of complex PTSD and a writer and journalist who covers addiction and recovery, I am intrigued by Jamie's new book. The recovering world is complex; many of us suffer with multiple disorders that are intertwined with our deepest wounds. And sadly, only a few recovery pathways delve into the heart of our trauma — most merely touch the surface and focus instead on presence and looking ahead. The bittersweet part of recovery is that until we heal those wounds, it is nearly impossible to enjoy the present. Jamie's book beautifully navigates the crucial element of processing trauma in the most creative way I've ever seen. Reviewing the book gave me not only the honor of enjoying her words before they are published, but I was also able to incorporate play and mindfulness into my long-term trauma recovery in a new way — a way that in-depth psychotherapy has yet to touch. In just a few short weeks, my creative outlets have expanded and my psyche and nervous system have thanked me. This book is deeply needed and one I will recommend to any recovering person."

—**Olivia Pennelle**, Journalist, *Liv's Recovery Kitchen*

"Dr. Marich has lovingly laid out a process to investigate expressive arts with courage and curiosity. The fact that this is also a way to mend trauma in ourselves is important but not so stressed that the healing of the wounds themselves becomes more crucial than the journey. The examples help make the process feel possible and the friendly way the book is written invites one to give it a try. I already have a list of people who will enjoy this book; I highly recommend it."

—**Kyczy Hawk**, E-RYT-500, Author of *Yoga and the Twelve Step Path* and *Yogic Tools for Recovery*

"Dr. Jamie Marich takes readers on a powerful journey of self-exploration using expressive arts with a trauma-focused lens. Her exercises are carefully thought out and smoothly progress through each phase of healing. This is a must-read for individuals in all stages of readiness for change and regardless of perceived creative ability."

—**Suzanne Rutti**, MSW, LISW-S, Founder of Rutti Counseling & Consultation Services; Faculty Member, The Institute for Creative Mindfulness

Process NOT PERFECTION:

Expressive Arts Solutions for Trauma Recovery

JAMIE MARICH, PH.D., LPCC-S, REAT

Creative Mindfulness Media, the publishing home of The Institute for Creative Mindfulness, is committed to publishing exceptional materials addressing topics in the areas of trauma recovery, addiction recovery, and the use of embodied expressive arts approaches to create healing and wellness.

For more information, visit www.instituteforcreativemindfulness.com

Publisher: Creative Mindfulness Media
P.O. Box 8732
Warren, OH, U.S.A.

24 23 22 21 20 19 1 2 3 4 5

Library of Congress Cataloging-in-Publication Data

All photographs of Jamie Marich by Mary Riley (unless otherwise noted). Used with permission.

The Delight Song of Tsoai-talee by N. Scott Momaday used with permission. John Muir quote used with permission.

Every attempt has been made to contact copyright holders. If copyright holders have not been properly acknowledged please contact us. Creative Mindfulness Media will be happy to rectify the omission in future printings of this book.

Publisher's Note:
This book contains general information about wellness and recovery. The information is not medical advice. This book is not an alternative to medical advice from your doctor or other professional healthcare provider.

Our books represent the experiences and opinions of their authors only. Every effort has been made to ensure that events, institutions, and statistics presented in our books are accurate and up-to-date. To protect their privacy, the names of some of the people, places, and institutions in this book may have been changed.

Cover design by Michelle Tompkins based on a painting by Dr. Jamie Marich.

Interior design by Michelle Tompkins.

DEDICATION

For all of my "speechies" I coached between 1997-2011
Thank you for deepening my love of the expressive arts as healing

CONTENTS

SECTION I: PREPARING

SECTION I: PREPARING (CON'T)

SECTION II: DEEPENING

SECTION II: DEEPENING (CON'T)

SECTION II: DEEPENING (CON'T)

SECTION III: MANIFESTING

SECTION III: MANIFESTING (CON'T)

Acknowledgments

There's a lovely saying that teaches, "Go where you are celebrated, not where you are tolerated." I offer a deep bow of gratitude to those individuals in both my personal and professional life who have celebrated me and my weird, creative way of being in the world. This support continually creates a vital foundation for my expressive arts practice and teaching to grow. Now that the Institute for Creative Mindfulness is branching out into formally producing publications under the umbrella of Creative Mindfulness Media, I will likely be leaning into your support more than ever. Your faith in me has helped me to respond to this call along my journey as a teacher, writer, and community leader, and I smile when I think of you all.

Although my entire community of teachers, students, clients, colleagues, friends, and family who meet this definition are encompassed in my gratitude, I am pleased to mention several of you by name for your influence in this book and its process: Mary Riley (Chief Operations Officer, The Institute for Creative Mindfulness, my "life manager," soul sister, and friend), Michelle Tompkins (cover and graphic design, also a surrogate sister and member of my soul family), Kelsey Evans (social media manager, a graduate of the original *Dancing Mindfulness* class, the April Ludgate to my Leslie Knope), Ramona Skriiko (*Dancing Mindfulness* affiliate trainer and my long-time extra set of eyes), Erin Kelly (my student, sister/daughter, and traveling partner), Gregory Dean Tompkins (my favorite actor),

Dr. Stephen Dansiger (my collaborator and "ice dance partner" in our shared mission), Dr. Christine Valters Paintner (my personal expressive arts teacher and the embodiment of a healing sage) and Dan Mager (my dedicated editor and source of endless encouragement through the years).

Personal thanks go out to my "bonus" family: Lori Tincher, Ethan Reiter, Brendan Reiter, and Nic Gollner for getting me through one of the most difficult years of my life that formed the crucible in which this book was forged and written. To Coach Micah Bender—thank you for breaking away those stubborn layers of my defensive shell and teaching me how to stand up for myself. To my gifted village of healers and guides—Melissa Layer, Elizabeth Davis, Dr. Satyavani Gayatri, Dr. Erica Matthews, Dr. Michelle Thompson, and Baba Dharl Chintan —thank you for lighting the path. To Allison Bugzavich and Amber Stiles-Bodnar—your friendships sustain me every day. And to Adam Guerrieri—thank you for being my endless source of creative inspiration.

Lastly and most importantly, I extend a big hug and bow of gratitude to all of the members of the Institute for Creative Mindfulness community and circle of friends who contributed their talents to this book. Your work helped breathe a necessary dimension of soul into this offering, and I thank you for your vulnerability and your willingness.

Introduction

AN ORIENTATION TO TRAUMA, EXPRESSIVE ARTS, PROCESS, AND PRACTICE

Every breath you take is an expression of your body. Take a moment, if you are willing, and notice your breath. Listen to it. Feel it moving through you.

The sound your breath carries can release the worries of your mind and share the stories of your personal journey. If you'd like, take another breath or two. Once you establish a flow for your breathing, consciously make a sound of letting go as you exhale.

We are made to *express*– our joys, our sorrows, and all our emotions in between...

Whenever these elements such as breath, body, sound, and story fuse together, there is a spirit within you that comes to life! Expression is the gift that these essential elements of your human experience can share with the world. Holding back what nature intends us to express can result in dire consequences. If you were drawn to pick up this book and are now reading it, you have likely already realized this sobering truth.

We are made to *express*—our joys, our sorrows, and all our emotions in between, our thoughts, our dreams, our stories, our songs, our prayers, our visions, our missions, and our love. Because of traumatic or wounding experiences, we may internalize the message that what we need to express does not matter to the world. We may believe that our expressions are not important or valid. We may even think great harm will come to others if we express ourselves, or we may hold back out of fear that we won't be able to handle what will flow out of us.

Expression is the pathway to deep and lasting healing. This foundational message informs *Process Not Perfection* and the exploratory journey you are invited to take within its practices. There may be hang-ups to work through and old fear-based messages to confront. The good news is that expressive arts therapy practices can help you tackle this work. As your facilitating author, I will help you take the steps on this journey—a journey that begins with embracing the layers of wounding you intend to heal at this point in your life.

DO I REALLY HAVE TRAUMA?

Your own identification as a trauma survivor may have drawn you to this book in the first place. I encourage you to read the following section as an overview or as a review. You may get some additional insight into unhealed trauma and how it affects your quality of life. At the very least, it will put us on the same page about what trauma means and how it is addressed in the pages that follow.

People who have read my previous books and study with me identify with a variety of experiences. They ask me questions like, "Is what I went through really trauma? What about people who went to war, or who survived terrorist attacks? Aren't those the *real* traumas?" It's very normal for clients I treat and students I work with to minimize the impact of their wounding, largely because perpetrators of trauma often punctuate their offenses with comments like, "You don't know how good you have it." Many abusive parents who expose their children to an onslaught of interpersonal and developmental trauma will point to victims of so-called "real traumas" like war, famine, and natural disasters. They do this to invalidate their own children's cries of suffering and avoid taking responsibility for their own behaviors.

As a clinical trauma specialist and author, I have researched and written about the manifestations of unhealed trauma through diagnoses like post-traumatic stress disorder (PTSD), acute stress disorder, reactive attachment disorder, adjustment disorder, borderline personality disorder, and dissociative disorders. Conditions such as complex trauma and developmental trauma, while not yet formally included in American psychiatric diagnostic manuals, also merit attention in our larger conversations about how trauma shows up clinically. If you want to learn more about this area I encourage you to review the Appendix on trauma resources. Because this is not a clinical book, I am keeping the jargon to a minimum while providing a framework you can use to understand how the things keeping you stuck in life may be trauma-related. Additionally, this understanding may help you to recognize how approaching expressive arts practices with an open mind and an open heart can be the missing link in your healing.

Expression is the pathway to deep and lasting healing.

From a basic humanitarian perspective, my working definition of *trauma* is any unhealed wound—mental, emotional, physical, sexual, spiritual—that continues to cause problems in daily living or keeps us from growing into the fullness of our potential and radiance as human beings. Trauma comes from the Greek word *traumatikos,* which simply means "wound." I intone this metaphor of the wound throughout my teachings on trauma to professionals and other students who come to me for instruction in mindfulness, yoga, and other wellness pursuits. Wounds come in a variety of shapes and sizes. Some wounds, because of how deep they are and where they are located, may have fatal implications or cause lasting damage. However, if proper treatment is received close to the time of the injury, the lasting damage may be minimal. With continuing care, survivors can adapt to the injury and go on to live a full life.

All wounds require care. Yes, some wounds may require immediate professional care, whereas other wounds, like a simple cut or scrape on a healthy person, do not require rushing to the hospital. However, if this cut or scrape is not properly attended to (i.e., cleaned out, given time and space to heal) lasting complications can result. Infection can set in, and the wound can continue to reopen if exposed to other stressors. While we generally don't look at cuts and scrapes as being as bad as injuries like stabs or bone breaks, the point remains that the former can still cause lasting damage if they're not addressed in a timely manner. People with wounds that are labeled as "no big deal" can also be more prone to writing them off as insignificant when others tell them to "just get over it." When this happens, they may be deprived of the resources and space they need to heal.

The axiom that *hurt people hurt people* bears a great deal of truth.

Among the reasons I find the metaphor of trauma as *wounding* so useful is that everything we know about physical wounds and how they heal parallels other types of hurt—emotional, mental, sexual, and spiritual—and the larger realm of emotional healing.

For true healing to occur with any physical injury, repair must happen from the inside out. Sure, we often apply outside-in care for the sake of stabilization in the healing process (washing out the wound, applying bandages and/or antibacterial cream, getting stitches if needed). However, for deep healing to occur wounds need to be aired out and see the light of day. Outside intervention may be needed to get to the levels of scar tissue or other resulting internal damage. In cases of mental, emotional, or other types of trauma not easily seen, such deeper work is usually required, especially if the damage has been unattended. In many situations, we may have gotten so used to living with a rotting, festering wound from trauma or another adverse life experience that we have convinced ourselves it's no big deal.

In reality, we may be struggling like the injured athlete expected to go back into the game and play no matter what. In some cases, adrenaline and the pressure to do well may push us through to succeed despite our injuries. We may have concerns that others will label us weak if we stop to ask for help, or we may refrain from even asking for help in the first place to avoid this form of negative judgment.

Ironically, we often refuse to claim the traumatic origins of what keeps us stifled and stuck in life out of fear of hurting others—our parents, other relatives, our spouse/partner, our children, etc. We may also fear their chastisement for speaking up and taking actions necessary to heal. However, the axiom that *hurt people hurt people* bears a great deal of truth. Often, we keep our pain bottled up to protect others or ourselves, while we continue to bleed out, spreading our contaminants (metaphorically speaking) to those we love. Sometimes the people we seek to protect by *not* taking the steps to bring our wounds into the light end up being passive-aggressively wounded by other behaviors we manifest in trying to hold it all in.

The legacy of trauma can show up in a variety of symptoms and stuck points that play out in various life arenas. The diagnosis of PTSD specifically identifies four main areas of symptoms that can show up:

- Re-experiencing—flashbacks, nightmares, intrusive thought/images, physiological responses/body memories or psychological responses, like sudden panic
- Avoidance—problematic isolation, excessive use of alcohol, other drugs, or other self-reinforcing behaviors to block or numb the experience of uncomfortable emotions
- Cognition and mood—not remembering important aspects of a memory, internalizing problematic negative beliefs about oneself or the world, shifts in mood and symptoms that may look like what is normally labeled depression
- Arousal and reactivity—sudden outbursts of rage/anger, hypervigilance, heightened startle responses, problems paying attention, difficulty falling or staying asleep, self-destructive behaviors

Some of these symptoms may resonate as part of your experience whether or not you've ever been diagnosed with PTSD or another trauma-related condition. If this is the first time you are encountering this material and it sounds like you, I encourage you to follow up with a qualified mental health professional trained in trauma. If you are already receiving professional care, I applaud you for engaging in this work. My hope is that this book and the content within it can help you—whether you are already on your healing journey or you are thinking about starting on one.

Process Not Perfection is designed for anyone wanting to embrace the expressive arts as a partner on the road toward healing. Expressive arts emphasize working with internalized negative beliefs about yourself and the world that you may carry due to unhealed trauma. In my experience as a clinical and a wellness professional, many individuals struggle with these beliefs, regardless of whether they have been formally diagnosed with PTSD. To be clear, having a clinical diagnosis is not required to address a trauma or unhealed wounding that is keeping you stuck. I wrote this book for all of us who are feeling stuck in any combination of negative messages instilled by traumatic experiences, abusive figures, unhealthy or misguided loved ones, or the culture at large:

- *I am not good enough.*
- *I should have done something more.*
- *I am defective.*
- *My body is ugly.*
- *I am cursed or damned.*
- *No one can be trusted.*
- *I do not belong.*
- *I am permanently damaged.*
- *I have to be perfect.*
- *I have to please everyone.*
- *Women are supposed to look and act like ladies.*

- *Real men don't feel feelings.*
- *I must be in a romantic relationship to have true value.*
- *Only straight relationships are normal/honored by God.*

Do any of these resonate for you? And this is a short list, meant to offer only some examples. In the trauma therapy tradition from which I primarily teach, eye movement desensitization and reprocessing (EMDR), we generally discuss these messages as falling into one of five major themes: responsibility, safety, choice, power, and value.

Here is an example core belief, or cognition, in each of the five categories. Perhaps notice which thematic areas seem like your biggest stuck points related to healing and manifesting the life you wish to live:

- Responsibility ("I should have known better.")
- Safety ("I am always in danger.")
- Choice ("I have no options.")
- Power ("I cannot succeed.")
- Value ("I am worthless.")

Throughout this book I will encourage you to *listen with your body*. This is an invitation to get out of the rational tendencies we have as human beings to try and make sense of what happened to us or to figure out what is "wrong" with us. We often engage in this pursuit to avoid digging deep and feeling the feelings and connecting with our body in the way we need to in order to transform the belief into something more adaptive; something that better serves our intentions for living. To try out what it means to listen with your body, scan the above bullet pointed list of themes: responsibility, safety, choice, power, and value. Notice which of these feel unsettling. Which theme (or themes) cause you to feel a little jumpy, uneasy, or maybe even nauseous. Listening with your body can also mean an automatic, intuitive knowing. For instance, you may read the sample belief attached to a certain theme or themes and instantly relate in the spirit of, "Yup, that's me." If that's your response, honor it without trying to rationalize it away.

WHAT ARE THE EXPRESSIVE ARTS AND HOW CAN THEY HELP ME?

Some examples of expressive arts practices include, but are of course not limited to:

- Dancing and mindful movement
- Visual arts (painting, drawing, collage, mixed media, pottery, sculpture)
- Writing (short stories, novels, other fiction, poetry, scenes, memoir, other non-fiction)
- Music (drumming, playing an instrument, songwriting, making playlists, and listening to music)
- Drama and spoken word performances
- Meditation and guided visualization
- Photography
- Filmmaking
- Fashion design and hair design
- Cooking, baking, and other forms of food styling
- Gardening

Any medium or personal practice that gives us a channel for expressing ourselves to the world, or the simple joy of expressing what we have kept locked tightly inside, holds merit as an expressive art form. One of the Latin root words from which we get the English word "express" is the same root from which we get the word *press*, as in the process of extracting juice from a hardened fruit through a device called a press. We press the fruit to get the delicious and nutrient-packed juice, and the pulp from the rest of the fruit has use in other recipes.

Engaging in any combination of expressive arts practices—the multi-modality being a vital part of what defines formal expressive arts therapy—takes us through a similar extraction and transformation. What results is the ability of our vital, metaphorical fruits to be used to their fullest and most nourishing potential.

True expressive arts therapy (the more clinical term) or expressive arts (the more generalist term which implies that the practices can be adapted to a variety of educational or wellness venues) challenges us to use the whole fruit basket. This doesn't just mean exploring the different aspects of ourselves, it means embracing as many of the expressive practices available to us as possible. If you have ever used a juicer or juice press, this corresponds to the process of exploring all the different flavor combinations available with various fruits and vegetables. The expressive arts challenge us to work with as many practices as we are willing to engage and to notice what the multi-modal and inter-modal connections may reveal.

"Oh no! Does that mean I have to dance?!?!?!"

You may be getting nervous and saying something like this to yourself if dance frightens you.

Maybe you are an avid dancer so your protest may take the shape of, "Yikes, I have to make art! I can't draw to save my life. I can barely draw a stick figure."

"Writing!?!?! I can't write. I barely passed my language arts classes in school. How am I supposed to write?"

As a trauma-focused expressive arts therapist and expressive arts practitioner myself, trust me, I've heard them all. I've even made excuses myself over the years. The beauty of expressive arts and the multi-modal buffet of practices and options it inspires is that we can begin to practice expressive arts with whichever modality we are most comfortable. However, the real challenges and growth opportunities often arise when we endeavor to explore those practices we initially resist.

Staying with the fruit and vegetable metaphor, consider this: I did not like tomatoes as a child. Their beautiful red color fascinated me, especially the tomatoes that came from my grandfather's lush garden. I liked tomato-based products like ketchup and spaghetti sauce, but whenever I tried to eat an actual tomato, I spit it out. When I was about 12, one of the beefsteak tomatoes my grandfather expertly cultivated in his garden just looked too beautiful and I decided to experiment. I put it on a hamburger and doused it with ketchup. I took a bite, savored it, and didn't directly notice the tomato yet felt very happy that I was letting myself eat something so pretty. I finished the entire hamburger. I continued to eat tomatoes this way and by summer's end, I let myself try eating a tomato on its own, seasoned with just a bit of table salt.

I loved it.

To this day I adore eating tomatoes of all varieties in a wide range of presentations—on their own, in salads, on buttered toast, and in many other ways I steered clear of as a child.

I hope that engaging in the expressive arts practices and processes presented in this book may have a similar effect on you when it comes to exploring your *edge*—those places outside of your comfort zone. The expressive arts, like my hamburger and ketchup, allow us to experience a practice we might otherwise shy away from in the larger context of a combined and more palatable process that makes the practice safer to approach. In the process, we may unexpectedly discover we love the practice, or at very least that it's more "okay" than we expected and we have something to learn about ourselves through engaging with it.

The formal field of expressive arts therapy and education is currently regulated by an organization called The Expressive Arts Therapy Association (IEATA), founded in 1994. I mention this not to bore you with a clinical detail, but rather to highlight something about their mission and vision I hope you find helpful as a reader and as a new expressive arts practitioner. IEATA recognizes that no one person invented expressive arts therapy; the 2017 IEATA conference was even themed *The Indigenous Roots of Expressive Arts Therapy* to honor the people of our first nations as truly the ones who identified practices like drumming, dancing, storytelling, song, meditation, and ceremony as healing. These form the basis for what we know as expressive arts therapy today.

Practicing expressive arts is a way to connect to the most ancient and sacred pathways for healing that exist on our planet and within our human experience. There are a collection of notable scholars and practitioners from various parts of the world who have played pivotal roles in developing what we now call expressive arts therapy. Two of my favorite leaders in the development of the modern-day field of expressive arts are Angeles Arrien and Natalie Rogers.

Arrien, whose specialty is studying the healing arts of indigenous peoples, wrote *The Four Fold Way: Walking the Paths of the Warrior, Teacher, Healer, and Visionary* [1]. In a popular passage from this book that I often use in my teaching, she introduces us to the concept of the four, universally healing salves—storytelling, singing, dancing, and silence. She posits that the gifted healer restores the soul by using these healing salves, for the root causes of distress and *dis-ease* are when we:

- stop singing
- stop dancing
- are no longer enchanted by stories
- become uncomfortable with silence

In this book, you are challenged to become your own healer and work with these four healing salves in combination, guided by the expressive arts processes and practices presented in the following chapters.

My favorite expressive arts visionary is Natalie Rogers, the daughter of Carl Rogers. Carl Rogers is one of the pillars of modern-day psychotherapy. It's impossible to leave a graduate training program and not have at least one unit of content on Carl Rogers and the humanistic, person-centered approach to psychotherapy he pioneered. Many of the person-centered psychotherapy principles for which Carl Rogers is renowned were adopted by Natalie in her expressive arts therapy training programs.

1 Arrien, A. (2013). *The Four Fold Way: Walking the Paths of the Warrior, Teacher, Healer, and Visionary*. New York: Harper Collins, p. 54.

As explained in her landmark book *The Creative Connection: Expressive Arts as Healing* [2], there are three main conditions that foster creativity within an individual. The first is psychological safety, which we experience when, as an expressive arts practitioner, we are accepted as being of unconditional worth. We also experience this when external evaluation of our work is absent, and when we feel understood in a spirit of empathetic connection. The second condition is psychological freedom—a state that can result in expressive worth when we are given many options for exploration. Freedom can also result when we are invited, rather than commanded, to try out new things. The third condition is to engage in experiences that stimulate us and challenge us. Expressive arts work naturally allows for this because we are invited to explore, to the degree we are willing and able, those practices and processes that may feel outside of our comfort zones when we begin. Yet engaging in the practices that bring up some discomfort—and coming into contact with our *edge*—is often where we find the most nourishing metaphorical juice for our healing needs.

To get the most out of your developing expressive arts practice, I would like you to discard any ideas you may have that expressive arts work or formal expressive arts therapy is about creating "good" art that will hang in a museum, or producing high-quality movement choreographies that belong on the stage. True, some of you may identify as artists and perhaps even make a living with your craft. Even if you identify as such, I encourage you to release any trappings of those external or performance-based metrics to truly engage with the work in this book.

An unexpected result of engaging in the processes described here may be a flourishing in your professional work. Please don't make that the focus of this journey. A major feature of expressive arts is to focus on process, not product. Release any obsession with or fixation on outcome. Enjoy the journey and you will find healing in the process.

---

[2] Rogers, N. (1993). *The Creative Connection: Expressive Arts as Healing*. Palo Alto, CA: Science & Behavior Books, Inc.

There are many reasons why engaging in expressive arts practices and processes can assist in your healing from trauma and its legacy. The focus that expressive arts puts on process and organic unfolding instead of output and analysis offers multiple, valuable learning experiences about the importance of non-striving in recovery, whether that recovery relates to addiction, traumatic injury, another mental health condition, or all of the above. Through practicing non-striving and working with some of the challenges you encounter in this practice of not forcing outcomes, you will hopefully experience a greater sense of self-compassion. A major vehicle for healing from the legacy of trauma and transforming negative core beliefs is to allow ourselves to feel the emotions we've traditionally stuffed. A well-worn cliché used in holistic circles informs us, *if you can feel, you can heal.*

I know, much easier said than done!

I get it. I'm a trauma survivor too. Burying emotion likely developed as a survival strategy for you at some point in your life so why on earth would you want to risk giving this up?

On this journey you will decide for yourself if the risk of feeling is worth it for you. There are many people who have embarked on this work who can share their experience, strength, and hope with you about how vital and essential it has been to feel the full range of emotions. My intention is to issue an invitation to explore the lushness of what expressive arts therapy offers. Expressive arts practices can help ease you into experiencing challenging emotions and help you develop healthy ways to contain and manage them so they don't overwhelm you or become a liability in certain areas of your life. Some of the first processes and practices in this book are designed to help you work with emotional containment and management and then learn how to express difficult emotions as safely as possible.

Finally, expressive arts practices are action-based steps you can take that use all the senses and their possible combinations. Expressive arts allow you to work with all areas of the brain affected by unhealed traumatic experience. The emotional charge that accompanies unhealed traumatic memories and those pesky internalized negative beliefs about ourselves is primarily limbic in nature. The limbic brain, sometimes called the middle brain, cannot be accessed using words alone. Therefore, you may not be able to talk about what happened to you—there may simply be no words to express it. For some survivors of trauma, you may be able to explain in exquisite detail what happened to you, and yet you've never truly healed because you still engage in some of the same self-defeating behaviors. Your rational head may know what's wrong, but your emotions and body are still stuck. There's a good reason for that—we need action-based, emotionally-focused, and embodied interventions to heal ourselves totally.

Expressive arts practices can complement many well-established interventions for trauma-focused care (e.g., EMDR therapy, cognitive-behavioral therapy, dialectical behavior therapy, Gestalt therapy, psychodynamic psychotherapy, or any of the new wave somatic therapies for processing trauma). The expressive arts offer creative adjuncts for building resources that allow you to feel stable enough to proceed with the deeper work that your therapist may recommend. You may also find the practices and processes presented in this book to be helpful in between sessions—as resources to help you further tolerate, in a healthy way, what may be moving and shifting for you in your therapeutic journey. You do not have to be working with a professional therapist to use *Process Not Perfection*. However, if you are engaged with a therapist, I highly recommend showing them this book and getting their feedback on whether working through it at this time would be helpful for you.

A NOTE ABOUT TERMINOLOGY AND HOW TO USE THIS BOOK

You may have noticed that I've only used the words creative or creativity a few times so far. Although there are some clinical professionals who describe themselves as Creative Arts Therapists (this is a licensed discipline in some states), I have long preferred the word *expressive* to *creative* in approaching this work. Of course, there will inevitably be overlap. As you engage in expressive arts practices, I hope that you tap into your internal sense of creativity and the potential to bring something to life that wasn't there when you began this work. I view being creative as bringing something to life, and I find this to be empowering for survivors of trauma.

However, too many people I have worked with over the years have gotten hung up on the word *creative*. I've had many clients say, "I'm not very creative," because they received a message along the way that being creative means you must have produced something original. At some point, creativity became associated with originality or radical innovation; so many individuals assume that they cannot possibly be creative. I vividly recall a horrible comment a parent of a former student stated to her face. This happened during one of my episodes as a high school speech and debate coach. I was talking to the student and her parent about the possibility of her entering tournaments in a category called Original Oratory, where the student is challenged to write and deliver a 10-minute informative yet motivational speech. The parent replied in disgust, "Original? She doesn't have an original bone in her body or an original thought in her head. She just knows how to bullshit."

I was too shut down by his crudeness at the time to respond intelligently. To make amends for not being able to defend her birthright as a lovely, creative young woman, I've dedicated my life to empowering others through my work as an expressive arts therapist. I use the words creative and expressive interchangeably in this book, since I believe that we all have the capacity to birth new creations and we all have something to express. That being said, I discovered in my work with clients that the word *expressive* is much gentler. It doesn't come with the societally programmed messaging that to be creative means you must be the next Steve Jobs or Annie Liebowitz. You can use whichever term helps you approach this work more enthusiastically.
I believe that for most of us, who come to this work wrought with hang-ups

and negative belief systems, "expressive" is easier to embrace. I also believe the self-compassion inherent in this term helps to define the field of expressive arts and the approach of expressive arts therapy.

Throughout the book I will largely use the term *expressive arts* to describe the largest possible scope of our field and its work. For instance, even IEATA offers a credential for educators and consultants, suggesting that clinical therapists don't have the market cornered on using this work. Classroom teachers, wellness instructors, spiritual directors, and pastoral care providers are examples of other professions that can employ the expressive arts as vehicles for teaching and ministry.

My own mentor and primary teacher in the expressive arts, Christine Valters Paintner, holds a Ph.D. in Christian Spirituality and primarily works as a writer and retreat leader. I studied with her even after I had a Ph.D. in Counseling and had authored several books on trauma. I believe I learned just as much, if not more from her, than I did from any of my counseling professors or advanced trauma instructors. The message here is that we can all learn from each other, and the spirit of expressive arts promotes this collaborative exchange. My use of the term expressive arts suggests that we can all approach this work if we feel ready, within or outside of a professional therapeutic context. I may make an odd reference or two to *expressive arts therapy* in the book if what I am discussing is uniquely clinical.

There are two other terms with which I want to familiarize you in this orientation: practice and process. A *practice* is an action that we take to connect with a set intention. Individualized practices throughout the book may include the practice of contemplative photography while on a nature walk or the practice of guided visualization. There is a practice I routinely use called Taking It To The Page, a guided writing exploration that takes various forms depending on the process in which we're engaged. In expressive arts work, the noun *process* refers to a series of practices using multiple expressive forms in an interactive way. You may find yourself saying, "I'm in process right now."

In this book the processes are specifically structured for your learning. I generally include six different practices within one process composed along a healing theme like mindfulness or grounding. There is no set time limit within which you must complete a process. You may even find that the process with which I start you out in this book elicits ideas and flows you into other practices you've been introduced to or develop on your own. I encourage you to go with that openness and expansion if it should happen for you. Sometimes I spend months in process with a certain theme and I'm never quite sure when it will wrap up organically or flow to the next process I'm inspired to accept.

The verb *process* is also quite special and a major feature of expressive arts work. Being in process is embracing a spirit of going with the flow of whatever may reveal itself in your practices and not being bound to any set outcome or goal. The mindfulness attitude of non-striving and the yogic concept of non-gripping (*aparigraha*) beautifully encompass what it means to be in process. You may set out to paint a rose and the strokes may not translate from your brain and hand to the canvas as you originally intended. Maybe with a spirit of non-judgment, you keep going with the strokes and what emerges is a beautiful, abstract rainbow-colored dove. What you see on the canvas may not be what you originally intended, yet something inside of you signals that this image is exactly what you were supposed to manifest. That rainbow dove may then lead to you writing a poem or dancing a dance in celebration. Who knows where the path will take you from there? This is the essence and the joy of being in process!

Being in process may be difficult for you, as it is for many survivors of trauma. Going with the flow can come with challenges because somewhere we may have internalized that having a plan and sticking to it is a way to keep ourselves safe. Your home of origin may have been characterized by radical unpredictability, so being in process can feel uneasy at first, especially with all this emphasis placed on not being attached to an outcome. We sometimes believe that if we keep our eyes on the prize of outcome that we will be more secure. If we develop a contingency plan to respond to every possible *what if*, then we won't get hurt. However, I ask you to consider how many times you have been let down because that intended result doesn't come to fruition, usually due to forces beyond your control.

Knowing that process may be a struggle for you, I've prepared a preliminary set of practices that invites you to explore where you stand with being in process—to effectively dip your toes into the work of this book before diving in fully. This opening process and related practices appear toward the end of this Introduction.

There are fifteen processes of 6-7 practices each, and many of the practices offer significant modifications or bonus practices that you can choose to explore. The processes are divided into three sections, and the choice of three sections is deliberate. In trauma-focused care, most practitioners, regardless of their primary clinical orientation, work within a three-stage model of care. This three-stage model goes all the way back to 1889 and the work of French hypnotherapist Pierre Janet. He recognized that before a person can fully go deep and address the source of what ails them, they must first have a set of tools they can use to calm or soothe themselves, as needed. Janet's work generally refers to this first stage as Stabilization, which corresponds with Section I of *Process Not Perfection.* The stage that Janet called liquidating traumatic memories, or what professionals may call *processing* traumatic memories (notice the expressive arts link) is generally defined by the going deeper, getting to the root of matters. Section II is a companion for this process of going deeper if you feel yourself to be ready (be sure to read Some Safety Tips Before You Begin at the end of this section). The final stage in the Janet model is reintegration with society, which links to Section III of this book. The processes of Section III are designed to help you transition into your daily life now that you've reshaped or at least begun to transform some of the toxic negative core beliefs that have kept you stuck.

I recommend that you work the sections of the book in the order presented for optimal flow and for your own sense of safety. However, if you are working with a professional therapist and they suggest otherwise, please consider their feedback. Moreover, if your own natural process seems to take you in another direction and you end up mixing and matching some of the order, I encourage you to trust your own judgment as long as you keep listening with your body. If you feel like you're pushing yourself too hard emotionally, honor that *edge* and come back to one of your grounding or containing practices. Seek support from others in your network of social and emotional support as you need to.

Please avoid rushing. Take your time with the practices. The other use of the term express—as in *express mail* or *express delivery*—does not apply here. You may stumble upon a paradox (as many of us have) that slow savoring through these practices offers the *express* route to deep and full healing, and it may help to expedite the progress you are making in traditional therapy. However, if you make the results and the speed the focus, you may miss the deepest healing gifts along the way.

There is no right or wrong way to engage in the processes and practices. You may elect to take one day each week to be with a new process, or you may work one practice each day as a morning or evening ritual. You may skip weeks in between practice.

To help illuminate many of the practices, I've included sample pieces from members of the Institute for Creative Mindfulness community and other willing readers who have connected with me online. I also feature a few of my own pieces. The inclusion of these pieces in certain practices is to offer you inspiration if you are feeling stuck and to give you a working guide in practices with which you may be unfamiliar. There is no pressure to imitate any of the work you see. This is one of the reasons I elected to use black and white photography throughout the book.

My hope is that you are not too influenced or "colored" by the experiences of others. Although I make the colored versions of many of these pieces accessible to you online, I encourage you not to look at these until you've engaged in the practice for yourself first. I have set up an online portal as a supplementary resource for *Process Not Perfection* at:

www.traumamadesimple.com/pnp

In addition to viewing the sample pieces in color, this portal will also give you access to video demonstrations of many of the meditation and movement-based skills that I present in the book.

My final guidance in completing this part of the orientation is to refrain from just reading the material. You will get very little out of this book if you do that. *Do*, experiment, take part in the processes, even if you've picked up the book in your role as a teacher or a clinician wanting to share expressive arts with others. I find it difficult to guide others on a journey I have not been on myself. Similarly, unless you've taken part in these practices and processes it will be much harder for you to guide others through them.

YOUR GUIDE FOR THE JOURNEY

One of my expressive arts students recently shared, "I came out of the womb with a paint brush in my hand." I shared in response, "I like it . . . I came out of the womb dancing to ABBA." Indeed, my mother took disco lessons when she was pregnant with me in the late seventies and I received much of that joy in utero. I adore moving my body in response to any kind of music that comes on, or to the music of my own breath and heartbeat that works within me. Yes, when ABBA comes on, I get extra special happy!

When I was about five years old, I discovered that a way to deal with the feelings I already had amongst my schoolmates that I was somehow different or odd was to dance when I got home. I had a Mickey Mouse Record Player in our basement that allowed me to play Disney versions of pop hits and I would dance and move as if I was on my own private stage. Family stressors and discord also started around this time and the gifts of dance, singing, and a lot of the dramatics that came with them for me, helped me to deal. Looking back at it now with years of therapeutic hindsight, I believe this practice was critical for me to be able to accept myself and my uniqueness enough to stay afloat in school and at home.

I had the good fortune of receiving lessons in many performing arts practices as a child: music, various types of dance, theater, and I also figure skated for a few years, which combined my interest in dance and theater. Speech and debate tournaments were a big part of my high school experience, and during several periods of my adult life I worked with high school students as a speech coach, primarily in prose-poetry reading and motivational speaking. During my undergraduate years in the American Studies & English department, I developed a love of film and directing. The expressive arts and the multi-modality of them all have been a part of my life from a very young age. It wasn't until I entered my own addiction recovery journey in 2002 that I began to see the therapeutic potential of expressive arts.

I came into my recovery and this field through the back door. I worked in humanitarian aid in Bosnia-Hercegovina from 2000-2003, primarily under the auspices of the Roman Catholic Parish of Medjugorje, a major pilgrimage site near Mostar. My family is Croatian, a main reason the region drew me after the brutal civil war of the 1990s. I learned that in teaching kids English, especially kids that were affected by unspeakable trauma and upheaval, it was much more productive to use songs, movies, skits, and dances than to rely on workbooks. While I worked in Bosnia I also learned how to play the guitar, a nice instrument to have as a vocalist, and after getting empowered with a few chords, I began writing songs about my experiences. My mentor, an American social worker named Janet Leff who helped set me on the path of addiction recovery by attending 12-step meetings, suggested that I go back to graduate school for clinical counseling.

During my first internship, I worked with a supervisor who was a gracious woman and a little too burned out to care what I did as a clinical intervention. I worked at an adolescent residential unit for mental illness. After I told her a little bit about myself she said, "You're a singer? You play guitar? Do music with them. Dance with them. It's got to work better than what we're doing here." During that experience I had the great privilege of putting my expressive arts teaching methods from Bosnia to use with disenfranchised teenagers. We sang, we danced, we painted, we wrote. To this day one of my proudest accomplishments as a clinician was organizing two concerts that summer that the kids performed for the entire hospital.

As I grew as a clinician interested in working with embodied and holistic methods for healing trauma and addiction, namely EMDR therapy, I always saw a pathway for working in the expressive arts to expand coping skills, as well as vehicles to enhance the other therapies I used. During my own experience as an EMDR client I developed a mindfulness meditation practice and eventually a yoga practice, which led to me creating a program in 2012 called *Dancing Mindfulness. Dancing Mindfulness* started as a community network of classes and has developed into a global movement with facilitators trained all around the world. In 2015, I wrote a book (with help from members of our community who shared their stories) that teaches people how to build and to cultivate a personal dancing mindfulness practice for healing, transformation, and wellness.

In 2014, I had the good fortune of meeting Christine Valters Paintner of Abbey of the Arts in Galway, Ireland. Christine, a perpetual student of conscious dance forms, sought me out for training in *Dancing Mindfulness*. Through her I discovered the formal field of expressive arts and expressive arts therapy; these fields provided a framework for what I've been blending into my clinical and personal wellness practices since the beginning. I enrolled in some formal retreat and course-based study with Christine and received my official Registered Expressive Arts Therapist (REAT) credential in 2016, the icing on the cake to celebrate my life-long love of expressive arts.

In my teaching world, I offer courses and retreats that are more technical, such as EMDR therapy and fundamentals of trauma, as well as those that are more expressive, like the *Dancing Mindfulness* facilitator course, and a variety of classes and retreats using the expressive arts as a healing modality. In *Process Not Perfection,* I am delighted to share with you the fruits (or to carry the metaphor, the fruit juices) of my teaching and explorations with clients and students alike.

Rest assured, I have engaged in each of these practices and processes myself and have had many of the doubts you are likely to experience. I long viewed the visual arts as my "weak link," believing I had no talent in this area. However, starting with a visual art I enjoyed the most (collage), I was able to embrace working with pastels, painting, and contemplative photography in a way I never thought possible. In recent years I've even reconnected with the filmmaking passions of my college days that I once brushed aside as a novel dream, and I use YouTube as a way to share many of my teachings and demonstrations with the world. The expressive arts can make it possible for dreams and for growth to come full circle.

SOME SAFETY TIPS BEFORE YOU BEGIN

- Honor your limits, both physical and emotional. Although expressive arts can challenge us to explore those areas outside of our comfort zones and beyond, I do not endorse forcing or striving. Develop the art of listening with your body, a process that I explain early in the section on trauma.
- If your body is telling you to stop, honor that. Establish a practice early on in your work that feels safest and most grounding for you and use that as a "retreat" practice if you need it. The opening

practices in Section I are designed to help you cultivate these pauses and retreats, which is why I recommend you go through this book in order.

- If you have a support system or people you identify as safe enough to confide in, let them know that you're engaging in this work. Use them regularly to check-in with as you need to, especially if you are feeling overwhelmed. They may even have a willingness to work through the practices and processes with you. The content of this book lends itself well to a book club or study group. If you have Internet access you are always welcome to connect with the Facebook group, *Dancing Mindfulness* and Expressive Arts Community Forum.
- Physical safety is important. If you choose to engage in some of the movement practices described in the processes, be sure that you've cleared a sufficient amount of space to not bump yourself on anything. If you're dancing on a hardwood floor, avoid wearing socks—either move barefoot or with footwear that has some grip, even shoes will work. Watch your pant length as well. If you have an injury or a chronic illness, I recommend getting clearance from your medical provider before engaging in any physical practices.
- Please don't feel like you must spend a lot of money to do this work. I give you some tips on where to get the materials suggested for many of the practices at lower prices. Most of what I teach can be done with what you may already have in your living space.
- I suggest that you start a fresh journal for this experience. Blank page journals are my favorite because you can mix writing and visual art in a more elegant way. However, if you need lined pages for support or such a notebook is all you have access to, that will work just fine.

PREPARATION PROCESS: IN PROCESS

Please take a moment to read this poem I wrote at the beginning of 2017 called *In Process*. I encourage you to read it slowly, giving yourself some space to practice not rushing. You may find that reading it aloud (rather than to yourself) helps you to slow down. Don't worry, you don't have to read it for anyone, the privacy of your own space works. You are doing this for you! I used to tell my speech students that if you think you're reading it at just the right pace, it's probably too fast. If you feel like you're being a little too deliberate and slow, it's likely just right! As you read, practice what it means to listen with your body. Notice what may feel unsettling or uncomfortable and where or how you experience that in your physical body. Notice which lines may spark some of that instant, intuitive knowing and pay deliberate attention to how you experience that knowing in your physical body.

Take a breath . . . and let's begin!

In Process

Works of art in gestation
Are often called
Works in progress
The slogans and inspirational
Clichés call for
Progress not perfection
We judge students and employees
With the metric of a
Progress report

What if we were to change
Every use of the work *progress*
With the word *process*?
What if works of art in
Gestation are called
Works in process?
What if we encouraged
People to focus on
Process not perfection?
What if our metrics of
Evaluation took on the tone of
Process report?
What if we were to live our lives in process?

All life could transform
Into a journey of art making,
Fueled by the expressive spirit
We could refrain from
Judging ourselves so harshly
And instead savor the unknown
From the unknown and yes,
Even from our mistakes
We can discover a new way of being
From what we once labeled failures
We may unearth a new solution,
A new way to solve a problem
By creating in the moment and
Not forcing the big picture
May we encounter the essence of meaning.

After you've slowly read the poem, aloud or to yourself, take out a journal or something to write with and free write on the following questions. Your responses do not have to be neat or organized. Challenge yourself to write at least a paragraph although you are certainly free to write more.

- What was it like to *listen with my body* as I read this poem?
- What challenges do I see myself encountering with the approaching expressive arts work as a *process*?
- Knowing myself, what internal or external resources can I use to help me embrace this challenge with an open mind and an open heart?

In trauma work, a resource is anything tangible or intangible that you can use in the service of your recovery, to help you along the way. Examples of resources include certain prayers, meditation strategies, people in your support system, existing coping skills, songs, hobbies, pets, or even fictional characters or historical figures from which you draw strength.

You may already have noticed that it would feel more natural for you to draw or to collage your resources for this journey of becoming more comfortable with being *in process*. I am going to encourage you to make your resources visual now—either through drawing or through making a collage. With collage work, use some of the magazines or scraps that you may have hanging around and notice which images speak to you—reminding you of or directly describing your resources. As a cost-saving hint, many public libraries are willing to discard of their old magazines to the general public. Also, consider making use of some of the scraps that we often end up throwing away in your living or workspace as well. They may take on new purpose in a collage.

Notice what comes up for you during this visual process, continuing in the same spirit of non-judgment. You can do this work in silence or play some of your favorite music. Music can be both an anchoring and inspiring resource in expressive arts work, and I will invite you to work with music as a final practice in this process. Either before or after you work with the visual practice, consider making a playlist (if you know how to use this technology on one of your devices) that represents your resources and the positive qualities (both internal and external) in your life right now. The music can be spiritual-inspirational or Heavy Metal Rock . . . or both. Our tastes and our needs are varied. Make this playlist and listen to it, and if you're so inclined, dance/move to it as you do the visual work or afterwards. If you do not know how to make a playlist, putting on your favorite radio station or one of your trusted CDs/cassette tapes can also do the trick. As long as you select this music with the intention of it being a resource or support in your journey, you are in the spirit of this process.

Notice that I gave some clear direction at the beginning of this process to get you started and then I offered some options for blending other practices. This flexibility is designed to ease you into the art of process by offering you some choices. In this preparatory process we worked with the practices of poetry reading, body reflection, writing, collage or other art making, and identifying music. What are you noticing now that you've dipped your toes into this work? Congratulations for taking the risk and responding to the invitation!

The other processes in this book are taught with more direction and detail. The teaching is intended to guide you through the specific practices in the order they are presented. Although I encourage you to follow this order and flow, you may mix and match practices if the flow of your own process dictates it or it feels safer to do so. I ask that you not just skip over practices because you don't feel like doing them. If that resistance arises, notice it, and maybe spend some more time in the previous practice to inspire you to move forward.

Section 1: PREPARING

Process one

GROUNDING

If you have ever been in therapy or treatment before, you've likely heard your provider talk about *grounding*, a vital skill in trauma recovery, mental health recovery, and addiction recovery. It's also very likely that at one time or another you looked at your treatment provider with a sense of confusion about what the word means! Let's discuss some ideas and definitions, including some insights on why grounding is such an important part of any recovery path, before launching into our first formal process.

While noticing the literal ground below can be a good place to start exploring the meaning of this skill, that definition may be incomplete for you. There can be times when you literally look down at your feet and know, at least in a rational sense, that you are in the here and now. However, other parts of your experience may be pulling you into the past or projecting you into the future. One of my favorite, comprehensive definitions of grounding comes from Margaret Postlewaite: *Coming into the here and now by using our bodily sensations.*[2]

In this process, we will explore many sensory channels and their combinations as we work through the various practices. It will be useful for you to observe and take notice of which senses, which experiences, and which practices are most powerful in bringing you home into the present moment. Keep an open mind and an open heart as experiences that resonate for you on one day or during one season of your life may change over time.

There are several reasons why the skill of grounding is vital to recovery, regardless of which path of recovery you are pursuing. Depending on where you are at in your journey, learning the skill of grounding and becoming familiar with it may feel like big, important work in and of itself. If that is where you are today and you are not concerned about going deeper yet, embrace where you are right now and focus on grounding. Even if you already know that deeper work is going to be required sooner rather than later to help you to reach your health, wellness, and recovery goals, having the ability to use a combination of senses and experiences to come back into the here and now, to return to equilibrium, is crucial. So many clients and students alike have expressed trepidation about feeling emotions and diving into trauma work because they fear it will overwhelm them or it may suck them in so completely, they won't be able to come back.

Therefore, we learn grounding first. More than that, we practice grounding in daily life to develop the confidence that no matter how many stressors may come at us, we can find our ground in the reality of the present moment. Join me on this discovery in the practices that follow.

---

[3] Postlewaite, M. (2016). "Grounding: Coming into the here and now by using our bodily sensations." In Scott Simon Fehr (Ed.), *101 interventions in Group Therapy* (2nd ed.) New York: Routledge, pp. 78-80.

PRACTICE ONE

GROUNDING TREE VISUALIZATION

A famous quote attributed to the late martial artist Bruce Lee teaches, "Notice that the stiffest tree is most easily cracked, while the bamboo or willow survives by bending with the wind." Trees can be powerful, metaphorical experiences for the practice of grounding. You may learn in your own experience with these first several practices, including the *Grounding Tree Visualization,* that trees have many lessons to teach us. Are you willing to listen?

- Whether you are sitting or standing, notice the connection of your feet to the ground below you. Take a few moments here. Maybe pump your feet back and forth a few times and then let them come to stillness. Really notice the connection.
- If this works for you, imagine that roots are coming out of your feet and shooting into the earth below you, like the roots of a tree.
- Notice the roots moving deep, deep, deep into the earth, through all of the different layers. Take a moment to just be with this experience. Think of yourself being firmly rooted in the earth, in the here-and-now.

MODIFICATION NOTES:

- ✓ You can name what kind of tree you are, such as an oak, a banyan, an elm, or a pine tree. This might make the process even more real for you!
- ✓ If you have earth elements around your office, such as essential oils like Cedarwood or Pine, or even a Mason jar full of dirt (try it, it smells like the "good earth"), consider bringing those in to this practice—it can add to the grounding experience.
- ✓ If you need a guided audio/video experience to help deepen your connection to this practice, go to: **www.traumamadesimple.com/pnp**

PRACTICE TWO

TREE POSE

In Hatha Yoga (the yoga of deliberate, physical postures), tree pose is one of the classic postures taught to develop balance. If you are already judging yourself along the lines of "I have terrible balance," rest assured, you have to start somewhere. When I began my own yoga practice over ten years ago, even after having been a figure skater in my youth, I was shocked by how poor my balance was. Over time, through staying patient and non-judgmental with myself and the process, I acquired a much better sense of balance.

Some days the quality of the balance can still feel challenged, and that's okay. Practicing yoga poses is never about being perfect. Rather, allow the poses to teach you about life and how you relate to life. In that spirit, please be gentle with yourself and give tree pose a try:

- Begin in a posture of standing meditation, preferably keeping your eyes open. Notice the connection of your feet to the ground below you. If you can, think about an energetic connection moving up from the ground into your feet, up your legs, and through the rest of your body, keeping you in the here-and-now.
- As you feel ready, shift the weight slightly to your right leg. You can use a chair or a wall to help you for balance at any point in this pose. You can also use your arms in whatever way works for you to help with balance.

- Once you experience reasonable steadiness on the right leg, turn the left foot out, placing the left heel on your right ankle. Your left knee also turns out slightly, moving away from your body.
- You can keep the pose here or if you want more challenge, you can also place the left foot against the side of your right lower leg. The knee is still turned away from the body. Continue to use the wall or chair for balance as needed. If you try the pose at this "setting" and become frustrated, go back to the lower setting with the foot against the ankle or give yourself permission to use the chair or wall. Using these assists does not diminish the value of the pose.
- For maximum challenge you can place the left foot against the right inner thigh, keeping the knee turned out. It is very important not to place the foot directly against the knee—if you can't bring the foot to the upper leg; it's perfectly fine to keep it at the lower position.
- Repeat the same process, using the left leg as your foundation. Notice any differences you may experience shifting sides. It's completely normal for the experience to feel different on the other side.
- Starting with one attempt at the pose on each side of your body is fabulous. As you become more familiar with the pose, see if you can work up to three attempts, alternating right and left sides.

MODIFICATION NOTES:

✓ If standing up and doing this exercise feels too much to you at first (or if injury or disability inhibits you from standing up), you can achieve the same tree-shape posture laying down on a yoga mat or even in your bed. Laying down, keep one leg straight, as if you were standing, and turn the knee of the other leg out, bringing the sole of your foot to your ankle, calf, or thigh.

✓ See the photos that follow for additional guidance as needed.

✓ If you need additional instruction and require more visual cuing, go to: **www.traumamadesimple.com/pnp**

TREE POSE VARIATIONS

Tree Pose: Ankle Variation

Tree Pose: Thigh Variation

Tree Pose: Calf Variation

Tree Pose: Half Lotus Variation

PRACTICE THREE

MOVING THE BRANCHES

American naturalist John Muir once observed, "I never met a discontented tree. They grip the ground as though they liked it, and though fast rooted they travel about as far as we do. They go wandering forth in all directions with every wind, going and coming like ourselves, traveling with us around the sun two million miles a day, and through space, heaven knows how fast and how far."[4]

In this next practice, let us continue to work with the wisdom of the tree as we play with the concept of moving the branches. Perhaps think of your arms, head, and other limbs as branches of the tree meeting the winds of life. Notice what you notice about how you may respond to the reality of the wind, a powerful metaphor for the flow of life and all that it brings.

- In this *Dancing Mindfulness*-inspired practice, we'll first start in tree pose, at whatever level or setting you can comfortably maintain.
- Deliberately start with the arms in a steady position (e.g., hands together at heart's center/prayer, hands gently at the sides, hands in "okay" position at the sides)
- As you feel steadier, begin to move the arms away from the body or above the head. If you are using the wall or a chair for balance, keep one arm on the wall and begin moving the free arm.

[4] Wolfe, L.N. (1979). *John of the Mountains: The Unpublished Journals of John Muir.* Madison, WI: University of Wisconsin Press, p. 321.

- Think of what it means for branches to grow and to sway—if possible, let yourself embody that experience.
- If you like, put on music—music/sound that conjures up associations to nature settings with trees can be nice. You may even have music on hand that directly references trees.
- Continue with the process of moving the branches and if it feels organic, begin to move through space, letting a dance or other creative movement unfold.
- Focus on the sensation of still being grounded and connected to the earth, even while moving.
- Notice your experience, knowing that you can come back to standard tree pose or standing meditation at any time.

MODIFICATION NOTE:

✓ This practice can be done standing up, sitting, or lying down. If you need to lie down for the practice, move your arms/branches above you so that your field of vision can notice what you are doing with your movement.

PRACTICE FOUR

GUSH ART

Before you engage with this next practice, it may be useful to take a few moments and silently think about what the word *gush* may mean to you.

For me, it means not having any deliberate direction or expectation. It is the pure art form of just *going with it,* literally making art outside of the lines. Just as we cannot predict where the flow of the wind or the breezes of life will take us, neither can we predict where the flow of our art is going to take us, or what it is going to teach us, if we let ourselves surrender to this process.

- *Gush art* is a term used in expressive arts therapy to suggest uncensored creation with art—notice what the word "gush" means for you and allow that to unfurl on the page using materials you have available (crayons, markers, pastels, paints, etc.). That is the only prompt you are going to receive for this practice: Get out the materials and go! Gush!
- As is the case with many forms of meditation, it can be useful to set a timer for the gush art experience. This can help you keep your focus on the process of the experience instead of the outcome. When the timer expires, check in and notice whatever it is you notice about the experience and/or move along to the next practice.
- *Gush art* can be done without much direction as a pure stream-of-consciousness activity, or you can set a theme to the experience.

In this case, working with the theme of tree or grounding for a set period of time is a nice option. Setting the timer can keep us from being too outcome oriented with this or other practices. When the timer rings, as they say on many of the cooking shows: Put it down and walk away. Observe that what you express in the set period is what the creation is meant to be in this moment.

- If you are inspired to continue it later, you may, although know that it's not a requirement. What you *gush* in this process may simply be meant to exist as an imprint of this present moment.

MODIFICATION NOTE:

✓ If the thought of "gushing" with all available materials feels too much for you at first, pick one medium or implement (crayons, colored pencils, or markers, etc.). Starting smaller may give you the extra comfort you need while still giving yourself sufficient challenge.

GUSH ART EXAMPLES

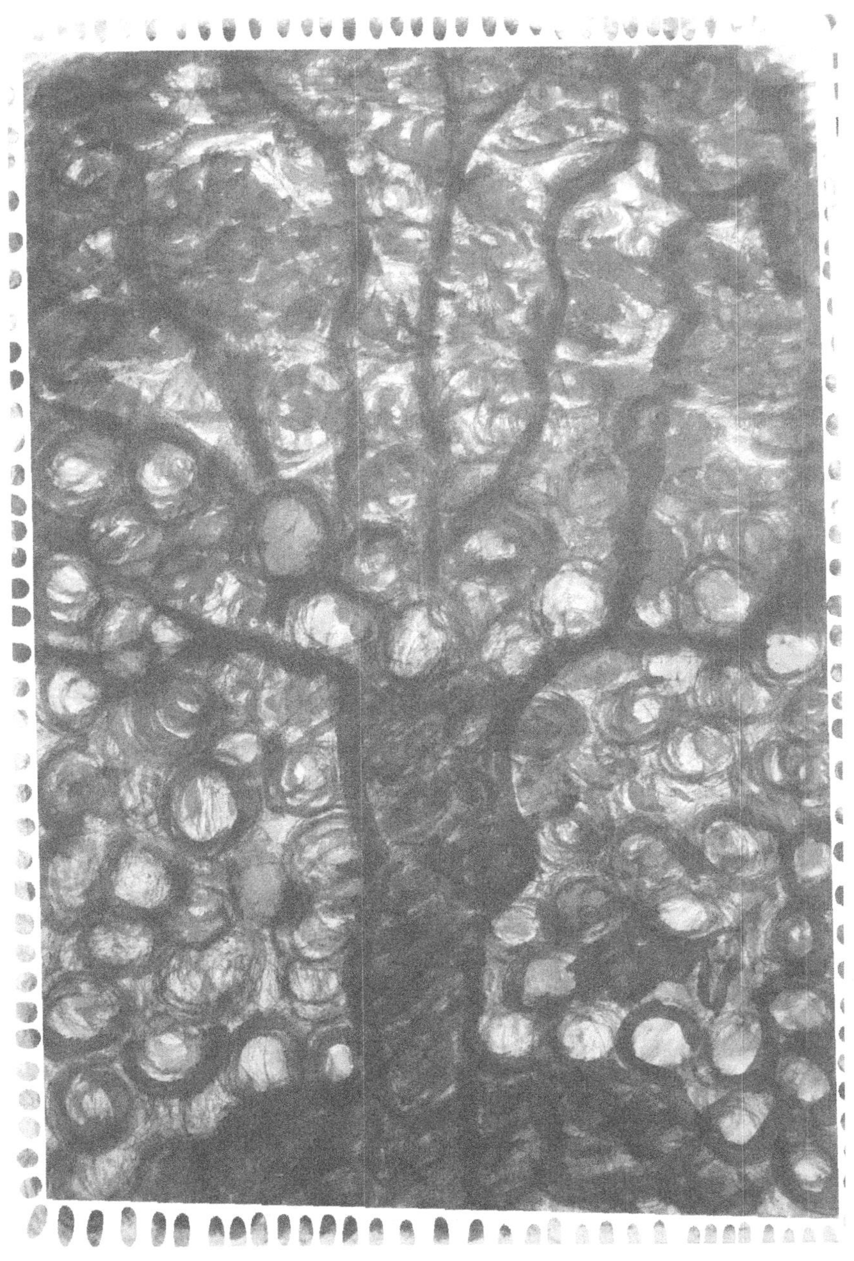

~ DR. JAMIE (PRAGYA) **MARICH**

~ ALEXIS RAE **BURROW**

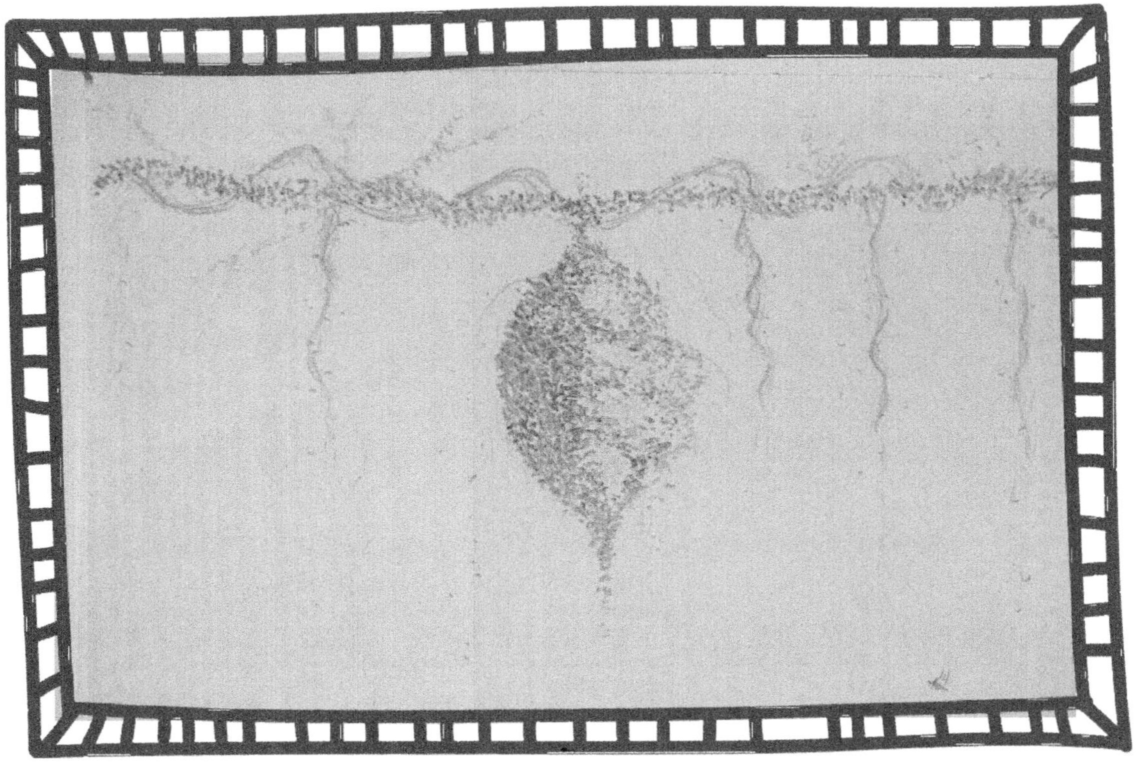

~ KATIE **GIFFORD**

~ PEYTON MARNIE **CRAM**

~ TRACEE **MOSS**

PRACTICE FIVE

TAKING IT TO THE PAGE

To continue the multi-art process, we will now move on to writing. There is a good chance that previous therapists or treatment providers have encouraged you to journal. If you work a 12-step program, it's likely that sponsors have had you write before: lists, inventories, step work. You may love to write, or you may despise it. Your feelings may exist somewhere in the middle. Regardless of your previous experiences with the written word, see if you can approach this expressive arts practice of writing with a beginner's mind.

- There are a variety of places that you can go with this writing experience, depending upon your group or the needs of the individual.
- Setting a timer for a period of free writing/journaling, or assigning time to work on poetry or a short story experience is an option. You may consider setting a timer to make sure that you keep writing and avoiding judging yourself too harshly. Even if what you're writing feels like nonsense, commit to writing for the period of time that you set. If the timer rings and you have the time to keep going, you may do so, or you can practice putting it down and walking away for now.
- A common technique in expressive arts therapy is to focus on the page and notice which element from the art making is attracting your attention most. Once you've noticed, take 3-5 minutes to write from the

perspective of that element (e.g., I am a tree, I am a green tree, I am tall and powerful, etc.). As alternatives, you can add qualities to the statements, such as "I bring blessings," or "I dance with the wind" (e.g., I am the green tree, I bring blessings), or think about those elements directly delivering messages to you (e.g., I am the green tree and I have come to tell you how beautiful you are).

- When the timer expires, engage in the same process with a second element on the page, making sure the time allowed is equal.
- In conclusion, allow 3-5 minutes for a dialogue to unfold between the two elements that you just spent some time writing on, not forcing an outcome, and notice whatever the dialogue may reveal.

MODIFICATION NOTE:

✓ For this and any writing practice in this book, you can choose to physically write in a paper journal using a pen or any other color implement, or you can type your writing using a computer or smartphone. I ask you to notice which method is most helpful for you to get in touch with your feelings and experiences. This may involve trying out all options and then deciding from there. Speaking for myself, I do most of my personal process in a handwritten journal format first and then will often word process it later if there's more to be explored.

TREE POETRY EXAMPLES

I Am The Tree

I come from the ground,
reaching down and out, touching
more than you can see

the each moves around me,
in me, feeding & protecting me
holding me in place &
encouraging me to be more

I stand strong and firm, course &
immobile, twisting & turning
in ways that only make sense to
me

I am a home for those both permanent &
transient. I take those that I can
and offer all that I am. I am scared and I am strong

I move & bend & break & survive.
I blossom & die & return, again & again
I am not defeated. I will protect, I will grow. I will change & adjust.

I will be here.

I am the Tree.

~ ALEXIS RAE **BURROW**

Gnarly

Rooted and tangled
Unapologetically beautifully rough
    Two in one
No need to decide, no choice to be made
I can be rooted and fly
I can flower and die

~ RACHEL **WEAVER**

Wild Heart Expressions

They tried to tame you.
For many seasons,
They cut away at your scraggly parts,
Plucked apart your uneven petals
Sheared back your branches
In attempts to fit you in their neat rows of hedges.
They called your tendrils ugly and a nuisance-
always sneaking to and fro.
Vines wild and far-reaching -
They tried to keep you small for so long.
You felt this was your duty-
 to blend in unnoticed,
to squeeze your shoulders into confined shrubbery, bordering an English garden.
Each morning they'd be back at it-
raking fingers through your weeds,

When these were what you needed to grow wild.
Heart, you were meant to express these beautiful seeds.
You were meant to grow free, untamed-
to sprout dandelions,
for tiny, white feathered petals to fly above in a flurry of wishes.
For roots to dive and search deep underground-
to mix and mingle with the earth, the dirt.
Making neighbors with the moss and berries.
Hosting bees and butterflies and ladybugs and long slimy earthworms.
You were meant to make the wind sing as she passes through your cattails,
to murmur through your tall grasses,
to whisper as she rushes over your heather.
You were made to be rough like bark,
smooth like the cap of mushroom.
Delicate as iris and dangerous as ivy.
You were meant to dance in the winds,
twirling as your seed falls to earth like samara, seedling of Elm and Maple.
Meant to collect silence like thick, boggy mud, softly holding all of Nature's
impressions like a secret to discover.
Wild heart, you were meant to be mysterious,
layered in thicket and winding through shadows.
Periwinkle petals a startling delight.
Silver threads of Spider's web twinkling in moonlight.
Thorned vines and briars and thistles.
Crooked stems, multi-colored buds, and blooms.
You were meant to come alive with passion,
Wild Heart,
never to fall still.

~ MEG **HARBIN**

PRACTICE SIX

HOLD YOUR GROUND

For some of us, grounding is best practiced by literally holding the ground. Maybe you like to go outside and lay in the grass, walk in your bare feet, run your hands through the sand or along trees or plants. A healer I worked with once literally advised me to go outside and hug a tree each morning as a deliberate, intentional connection with the earth, with nature, and with my sense of grounding. Although a variety of these direct contact points with nature may work for you in the spirit of this practice, consider this variation to wrap up our formal process on grounding:

- Holding an object with a hard or firm texture is a popular way for many people to connect with their sense of grounding and anchoring to the moment.
- Look around your house, your office, or whatever space you are in and start holding various objects in your hand. Notice the texture and the weight of them. While rocks, stones, and other objects with weight are conventionally used for this practice, literally anything can work that resonates with you as far as feeling a sense of connection to texture.
- Once you have found a texture you like, take as much time as you like (try at least a minute) and simply breathe as you notice the experience of the texture in your hand. Be present with the sensations and the connection.

- If you have nerve damage or other medical issues that make connecting with an object in your hand impossible, consider using your foot or another body part where you may have greater sensation to make contact with the object.
- To take this practice a step further into the expressive arts realm, consider having some stones on hand in your home or office that can easily be decorated with a Sharpie®/marker or other arts materials as your own personal processes may move you.
- Like with other art forms discussed in this book, you can decorate it, perhaps making the anchoring stone more meaningful for you. This process can be as simple as writing one word on the stone that is representative of a special resource—for example, "Trust," "Acceptance," "Strength," or "Faith".
- You may wish to conclude the practice with a simple affirmation such as, "Today I choose to hold my ground" as you look at the object in your hand and notice the weight/sensation of it against your skin.

MODIFICATION NOTE:

✓ Although taking a rock or another object generally works great for portability and carrying it with you into life, you can achieve the same spirit of this exercise by going outside and actually touching a tree. If you do that, notice its bark, the branches, the leaves, or the texture of any other fruit coming from the tree. Keep the texture as your focus and maybe even repeat one of the affirmations you developed as you engage in this practice. Like with many practices here, if you like it, you can turn it into a daily ritual.

OBJECT EXAMPLES

REFLECTION QUESTIONS FOLLOWING THE PROCESS OF GROUNDING

At the end of each chapter, I provide a series of reflection questions for your personal study. How you use them is largely up to you. Journaling on them in a conventional sense is an option, or you may choose to share your insights with a trusted friend, sponsor, fellow creative, or your therapist. In sharing your reflections or even the specific pieces you created in your process, it is important to release the attachment you may have to receiving positive feedback in the vein of, "Wow, what you made is so beautiful," or "You're such a great writer!" Ask your sharing partner, instead, what came up for them emotionally or what they related to as you share your work or your responses to these questions.

- Describe your personal experience with the process.

- What did you discover in your process?

- What did you learn about yourself in the process?

- What did you notice about judgment or self-criticism during the process?

- What role did the multi-modality of the art forms play in discovering what you discovered in your process?

- Which of the skills explored in this process can be applied to your overall trauma recovery or wellness plan?

Process two
BREATHING

Breath is life force dancing through us. Some days it may feel like your life force is trudging or moving very slowly, and some days you may not be very aware of your breath, let alone your "life force." As human beings, breath is vital to our survival, so vital that we sometimes forget how important it is. The typical adult takes anywhere from 15 to 20 breaths each minute—on the lower end that makes 20,000 breaths a day. Each year, the tally is anywhere from 7 to 8 million complete cycles of inhale-exhale.

Stress in our body often results from and is routinely worsened by not breathing deeply enough. The ill effects of hopelessness and lack of motivation that can plague us are made worse when we do not access the healing potential of our breath. In Eastern systems of medicine and wellness, being cut off from our vital life force, referred to as *prana* in yoga and several other traditions, explains why we can find ourselves overstressed and hyper-aroused. On the other end of the spectrum, this cut-off from prana can result in feeling lethargic, shut down, or otherwise hypo-aroused. Our breath, the carrier of our life force, is a marvelous gift that lives inside each of us. Living and breathing on autopilot is like saying we don't want this marvelously inherent present to help us deal with life and transform our experiences of life. Heck, many of us are too unaware or too indifferent to even unwrap this present!

In this process, we will be exploring various practices for embracing the gifts of our breath and using them to help us deal with life more effectively. You may have tried breathing exercises before, especially if you've seen a professional counselor, been to treatment, or attended a yoga class. If you like what you've learned about breath so far, my hope is that in this process you will explore some new ideas and practices in the spirit of beginner's mind. I've designed this process to integrate some creative and fun angles to working with breath, going beyond the standard instruction you may have received before. Perhaps you've tried and liked the gift of breath and yet you frequently forget to deepen the breath at the moments you most need it. This is akin to keeping the beautiful gift that we know can work unused! If this sounds like you, try to approach this practice as a way to become reacquainted with your breath and explore what blocks may be keeping you from using your breath to its maximum potential.

You may be the reader who can't stand deep breathing exercises, especially if you've tried them before and feel they didn't work. There are many reasons people may feel this way. Sometimes if breath work doesn't instantly relax us, we can jump to the conclusion that it will never work for us. Like many great healing strategies, breath work takes practice and that practice needs to be ongoing—exploring several different types of breathing and playing with possibilities and variations. Some people think that if breath strategies aren't working, they are doing it wrong and so must be flawed in this area. A client of mine once declared, "I'm such a screw up, I can't even breathe right!"

Although the practices shared within this process will give you some ideas and insights on proper technique and help the breath work to its maximum intended potential, there is no such thing as doing them "right." As Dr. Jon Kabat-Zinn, one of the leaders in the secular mindfulness movement and founder of the *Mindfulness-Based Stress Reduction program,* observes, "as long as you are breathing, there's more right with you than wrong with you."[5] As every yoga teacher I've ever studied with adds, "If you are breathing, you are already doing yoga!" I would emphasize that if you are aware of your breath right now as you read this, you are already engaged in the first practice of this process, so congratulations and welcome!

A final potential barrier I would like to address (and one that may apply to many readers) is the legitimate fear you may experience of your own breath. You may fear that your breath can make you too relaxed and thus spiral out of control. Many clients have shared with me over the years that breathing exercises can make them so relaxed they feel as though they can no longer be vigilant or protect themselves if they need to. Hypervigilance of this nature can be normal if you are early in your trauma recovery, and I want to validate that. However, I hope you don't let it discourage you from giving this process a try.

I can recommend a few strategies that may help you to feel safer and more supported. First, do these exercises with your eyes open. That way you can still see your surroundings. Moreover, closing the eyes may make you feel claustrophobic or too relaxed too quickly. The second major safeguard is to go slowly. With each breath practice in this process, start with 1-2 breaths, and then, if you are feeling unsteady go back to one of your grounding practices. Some of the most successful breath practices I've seen people develop start very slowly and grow over time. Be kind to yourself as you engage in this process of exploration. You can open the gift as slowly or as quickly as you like.

---

[5] Kabat-Zinn, J. (2013). *Full Catastrophe Living (revised edition): Using the Wisdom of Your Body and Mind to Face Stress, Pain, and Illness.* New York: Bantam Books.

PRACTICE ONE

MEETING YOUR BREATH

Many people set themselves up for frustration because they jump into doing deep breathing too quickly. This can be overwhelming, especially if your brain is not used to receiving so much oxygen. In this practice, we will begin very slowly by engaging in the simple practice of breath tracking—literally paying attention to your breath as it is right now, in these moments. This practice can be described as simple and yet not easy, so make sure that you are sufficiently grounded before tuning in and saying "hello" to your breath, as if you are meeting your breath for the first time.

- Come into a comfortable position that you can sustain for a few minutes. While it's common in meditation settings to sit cross-legged with your spine straight, how you sit in this practice is completely up to you. If you have a cushion to sit on, many people find that elevating the hips slightly is helpful. You also have the option to sit with your back against a wall or in a chair; if you elect this option, attempt to keep your feet on the ground if at all possible. You may lie down if you need to due to illness or injury, although I highly recommend that you first attempt this practice while seated.
- Find a space that is as quiet as possible so you can tune in and listen to your breath.

- Breathe naturally—you do not have to do anything special with your breath.
- Notice your breath as it naturally flows through your body, paying attention to every little detail.
- Notice the natural rising and falling of your stomach and chest on your inhale and your exhale. Notice if the breath makes a sound. Notice if it has a temperature: would you describe the breath as warm, cool, or neutral?
- How does the breath feel entering through your nostrils? Are there any other parts of your body that seem to draw your attention when you breathe? Are there any other subtle vibrations or sensations you are aware of when you breathe?
- Continue this practice for 3-5 minutes, setting a timer if possible.

MODIFICATION NOTES:

✓ Remember that the amount of time you spend in the practice, particularly during the first trial, is up to you. If 3-5 minutes seems overwhelming, start with one minute, or even 30 seconds.

✓ If you truly have difficulty staying focused on the breath, you can record yourself asking the questions presented above in this description and listen to them back on your phone or another recording device to help you stay guided.

✓ A classic teaching of the Buddha offers us another splendid guide for this practice: "As I breathe in, I know I am breathing in. As I breathe out, I know I am breathing out." Many people find using this teaching valuable, saying it to themselves as they inhale and exhale. Some of my clients and students adapt it simply by saying "In" to themselves as they inhale, and "Out" as they exhale.

PRACTICE TWO

WRITING A LETTER OR THANK YOU NOTE

Now that you are more fully acquainted with your breath, I invite you to use this practice to communicate in response to your breath. In many of our cultures, upon meeting someone for the first time, it is common to say "nice to meet you." If the first meeting was more extended, we may even send a quick note, email, or text expounding upon this sentiment. What is it you would like to say to your breath right now? You are not bound to follow the typical, clichéd "nice to meet you" vibe in any way. If you find the breath to be an intriguing or challenging new acquaintance or if you have some other things to say to the breath, especially if you have felt abandoned by or cut off from it, this practice is your chance to express those feelings.

- Get out a piece of paper or open to a blank page in your journal. You may even elect to find a blank greeting card or thank you card for this practice.
- Having just met or become reacquainted with your breath, express with words what you need to say. You can also use some symbols or drawings in your communication if words evade you.
- Take as much time as you need with this practice, although you may want to consider setting a timer for 10 minutes in order to prevent yourself from overthinking, obsessing about outcome, or getting too analytical.

MODIFICATION NOTES:

- ✓ Although you are encouraged to try this first as a written exploration, you also have the option of recording your spoken voice. In modern times we often send "voice texts" or recorded audio messages to people, so that is an option for your approach to this practice.
- ✓ Rest assured that your note or expression does not have to be long. A couple of lines or even a couple of words will suffice.

THANK YOU NOTE EXAMPLES

Dear Breath,

I know that I don't always give you the attention you deserve but I wanted to take a minute & thank you for always being there for me. I'm so lucky that you always seem to know when I need you most. I can always count on you.

Thank you, Lexi

~ ALEXIS RAE **BURROW**

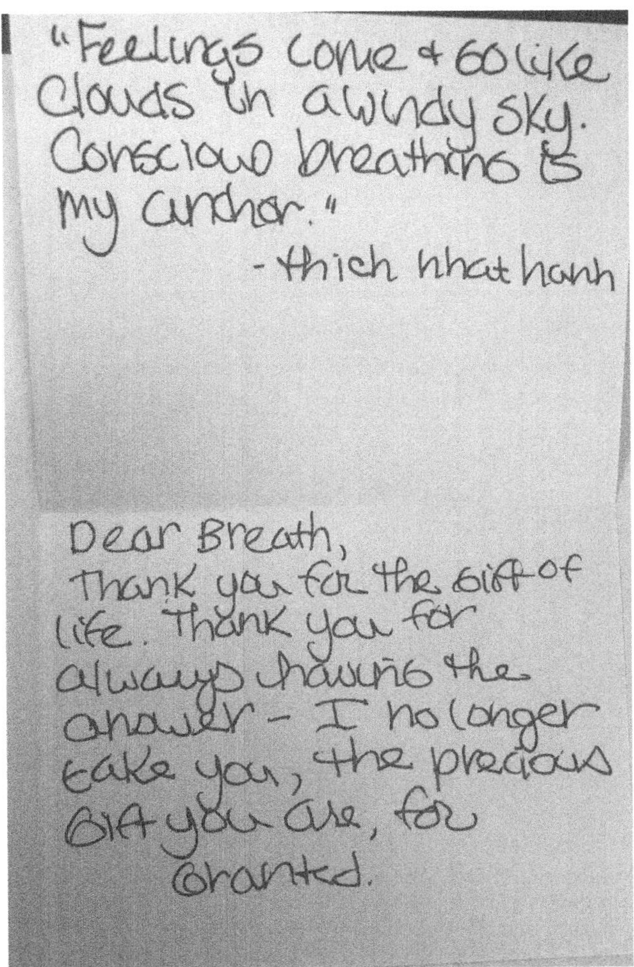

"Feelings come & go like clouds in a windy sky. Conscious breathing is my anchor."

- thich nhat hanh

Dear Breath,

Thank you for the gift of life. Thank you for always having the answer - I no longer take you, the precious gift you are, for granted.

~ TRACEE **MOSS**

PRACTICE THREE

BREATHING TO THE MUSIC

Some people find that breathing in silence is the most distracting and challenging aspect of getting acquainted with breath. While silence can be important for fully listening, it is not imperative. In this practice you are invited to encounter the breath once again, this time while listening to music. You may regard this practice as the act of breathing along to the music.

- Intentionally choose a piece of music for this practice. Some people like to pick songs or instrumentals that directly reference breath or elicit images of breath. There is no shortage of Top 40 songs that have referenced breathing over the years: Just go to Spotify, iTunes, or YouTube, type in "breath" or "breath songs" and you will literally have hundreds of options. Another method is to think of an instrument like the flute or the harp that reminds you of breath.
- You do not have to choose a song with direct connections to breath. You can pick any song that you like or you can access easily.
- Listen to the music you selected and as you do, notice what happens to your breath.
- For the remainder of the song, see if you can "breathe to the music," synchronizing the rhythm of your breath to how you are hearing the music and how it moves in your body.

- If you chose a more up-tempo song and it leaves you feeling more agitated at the end of the practice, try the practice again with a slower paced song.

MODIFICATION NOTES:

- ✓ Some people have difficulty listening to music and not dancing or moving in some way. If you notice movement rising in your body as you listen to the music that is wonderful. While you are encouraged to go with it, keep attention to your breath the primary focus.
- ✓ If you are so led, you may write your breath another letter or thank you note after this new practice and perhaps compare the qualities in the two notes.

PRACTICE FOUR

THE BREATH PRAYER OR POEM

The breath prayer is a contemplative Christian practice dating back to the 6th century. After a period of stillness, being especially mindful of the breath, the practitioner simply notices the first 3-5 words that come up. The words of your breath prayer may change over time as the breath allows, or you may find that the 3 to 5 word prayer serves as an anchor prayer for your ongoing practices. Some examples of well-known breath prayers in the Christian tradition include: *Holy Wisdom, guide me; Lord have mercy; Holy one, heal me.* Eastern practitioners may notice similarities to the practice of meditation and mantra. The Buddhist teaching *"As I breathe in, I know I'm breathing in; as I breathe out, I know I'm breathing out"* (referenced in Practice 1 of this Process) also qualifies as a breath prayer. I am calling this practice the Breath Prayer or Breath Poem, giving you the choice to approach it from the perspective you prefer. If the word "prayer" is tricky for you and brings up some unpleasant connotations, please approach this practice as a poem.

- Come into a comfortable position sitting or lying down that you can sustain for a few minutes.
- Tune in to the breath and really listen. You've spent the last few practices becoming acquainted with your breath, now listen to what the breath may have to say to you in return. Take as long as you like in this part of the practice.

- What are you noticing? Is a certain line or series of words revealing itself on the inhale and another on the exhale?
- Take a few moments to jot down on a piece of paper or in your journal the words that are revealed to you as you listen to the breath. This becomes your breath prayer or breath poem.

MODIFICATION NOTES:

✓ You can use music for this practice although you are highly encouraged to select an instrumental if you do. Lyrics may compete with the natural words that want to reveal themselves as you breathe.

✓ Length is not important. Some of the most potent breath prayers can be one line in and one line out (e.g., "Help"- inhale, "Me"- exhale)

THE BREATH PRAYER EXAMPLES

The breath dances
The dance breathes

~ DR. JAMIE (PRAGYA) **MARICH**

Breath's Purpose

Purposeful, with intent
Connect me to all that I need;
To a higher level of consciousness.
To a higher level of calmness,
Take me where I need to be.
Closing my eyes…
I fill myself with the most beautiful gift of life.
Purposeful breathing leads to my soul's purpose in life.
How blessed I feel.

~ TRACEE **MOSS**

PRACTICE FIVE

THE DANCING BREATH PRAYER OR POEM

Now that you have received your breath prayer or breath poem, consider expressing the words of your prayer through a simple movement sequence. If the word "dance" still brings up some blocks for you, regard this as a movement sequence or a gesture prayer, a common term used in liturgical dance.

- As you inhale and bring up the first line of your breath prayer, what movement or series of movements are flowing through your body?
- As you inhale and notice the second line of your breath prayer, what movement or series of movements are flowing through your body?
- If your breath prayer does not correspond with a specific inhale-exhale flow, that's okay. Your movements do not have to match the breath exactly. The imperative in this practice is that you allow your prayer or poem to be expressed with movement. Allow the movement to link with breath wherever possible.
- Continue with this practice for as long as you like, giving yourself at least three full rounds or repetitions of the movements.
- Take a moment after the movements stop to stand or sit in stillness. Notice the stillness following the movement, paying special attention to the quality of the breath in the stillness.

MODIFICATION NOTES:

- ✓ You can do this practice standing up, sitting down, or lying down. Notice what makes the most sense to your body and to your breath, and follow that guidance.
- ✓ You can do this practice along to music if you wish. As in Practice 4, avoid using songs with lyrics so that the words of your own breath prayer/poem serve as the main guide.

PRACTICE SIX

THE LEGEND OF THE BREATH (WRITING EXPLORATION)

One of my favorite stories from the Hindu tradition involves the deities of Sita and her husband Ram. In Hindu tradition, female and male deities are usually referenced together symbolizing the sacred unity between energy (feminine) and consciousness (masculine). One day the demon Ravana (who represents the ego mind) lured and captured Sita to exploit her for his own benefit. Ram called upon his devoted servant, the beloved monkey deity Hanuman, who represents the heart, the breath, and the ability to adapt or shapeshift to any situation depending on how he is needed. Hanuman called upon the forces of his entire monkey army and they found Sita at the southern tip of India, rescuing her so she could be reunited with her beloved. Hanuman's role in this story represents the power of the breath to reunite energy and consciousness. In this powerful fusion of energy and consciousness joined by the breath, order is restored and we are deeply healed.

Even if this story from this particular tradition does not speak to you, I encourage you to do some online searching or other research to explore how the breath and its emissaries are presented in the folklore and legends of other cultures. Many legends speak to the fire-breathing potential of dragons to destroy and annihilate, although sometimes this destruction is not intended for evil, but rather for the positive effects of clearing away blocks or vanquishing villains. Other legends reference ghosts and other mythical creatures gaining sustenance by stealing the breath of human beings, a testament to how coveted the human breath is because of the power it contains. In many of the creation stories in global folklore, wind gods like Enlil (symbolizing breath) in the Sumerian tradition used their breath to separate the heavens and the earth, making life possible for the human race.

- In this practice, you are invited to write your own story, legend, or myth about the powerful and healing potential of the breath. Allow the characters that develop in your story to symbolize different qualities, like Hanuman representing the rescue and integrative potential of the breath in the opening example.
- You can do some of your own research online or using other sources, although that is not required if your expressive juices are already flowing. You may find that doing additional research negatively impacts your organic process.
- You do not have to use characters from specific religions, cultures, or legends. Make this story totally original if you wish, although you are free to draw upon other sources for inspiration.
- If the breath ends up getting taken or stolen in your story, how is it discovered and restored?
- If an ambassador or character symbolizing breath in your story saves the day and plays the role of hero, what do you notice about your own breath as this plot point develops and you bring it into existence on paper?
- Take as much time as you need for the practice, even if this unfolds over several days.

MODIFICATION NOTES:

- ✓ There is no length minimum or maximum to your story. Some of the most impactful stories, legends, fables, and myths are less than a paragraph.
- ✓ If telling this story visually makes more sense to you, bring in an art medium like drawing or painting in place of, or in addition to, the writing.
- ✓ Vocalizing the story may also make more sense for you than writing it. If so, record yourself telling the story in place of, or in addition to, the writing. Reading your own words after writing them can be a powerful experience.

THE LEGEND OF THE BREATH EXAMPLES

Fink, a dryad of note, loved to stay with her folk in the mountains.
The air was different here & she spent hours dancing on the wind she would jump among the trees allowing their gossip to reach her ears.
That is how she kept up with the humans.

Humans would travel to her mountain ranges from all over.
For peace & quiet & to breathe the fresh air.
Sometimes the trees would gossip about the humans & Fink would become so enthralled she would visit the humans.
If she liked them enough she would leave some of her with them as a calling card to remind them of her mountains, the trees & the fresh air.

~ ALEXIS RAE **BURROW**

Wildwoods Breath

"You have no idea what it is that you're missing," Juniper growled.

"I know exactly what I've been missing!" Imogen was growing angry, it seemed to be the only emotion she could experience lately. She couldn't get over her mother's deceit, the Wildwoods theft, and all she had missed. She was weary. Clenching her fists, she faced Juniper head on, clenching her jaw and sucking down her exhaustion.

Juniper's voice softened, the hard edges of her face relaxing as she frowned, "Little girl, I don't think you realize how broken you are." Juniper extended her hand. "Here, let me show you," her hand patiently remained poised, waiting for her to take it. Imogen took a step back, caught off guard and eyed the woman standing before her. Bringing her arms to her chest and hugging herself, she dropped her head. Her anger falling away to despair. The desire to go home stirred in her chest and forget about the whole journey was enticing.

It felt like a lifetime, but Juniper remained stationed in front of her, waiting with her neutral expression. She approached her and slowly placed her hand into Juniper's. She noticed the woman' s callouses from a lifetime of work and sought comfort in the small contact. Something about the roughness reminded her of grounding. Before she could finish her thought, the air around their hands began to shift and warm. Her eyes widened as she looked from their hands to Juniper and back to the hands. It was almost like she could see the breeze whipping around their hands like a ball. Silver. Their hands were glowing silver. Her gaze traced up Juniper's silver glowing arm and it was turning wispy. She swore she could see the chair through her. Juniper's hair danced in tune with the breeze swirling around them. The last thing she noticed was her eyes. A bright silver rim around her iris pierced through Imogen and she tried to gasp but couldn't fully inhale. She was stuck in a choke.

She began to cough and tried to pull away, but Juniper began gripping her hand tighter the more she tugged away. "Let go," she managed between gasps. Juniper continued to grip her hand, even as Imogen fell to her knees. Tears stung her eyes, making her vision blurry. The funnel of air began to travel up her arm, its coolness causing the hair on her arms to stand at attention. Even though it was cool, there was a sense of comfort trickling up her arm. Her muscles were relaxing with every area the breeze touched. Managing to open her eyes, she thought her vision was going. The lack of air was about to kill her. Her arm looked wispy, just like Juniper's.

Her vision began to blacken around the edges and swaying on her knees. The tunnel of her vision only saw the shocked expression on Juniper's face as her lungs greedily accepted a full breath and she had the feeling of free falling. She was free falling. The weightlessness wrapped itself around her body and overtook her senses. Before she knew it, she hit the table behind her, shattering the glass top. The lights were out, shattered as well.

Fumbling around in the dark, grasping at anything that could steady her, she pulled herself up with the table frame. She let the perspiration on her forehead roll down her temples and felt sweat roll down her spine and embraced the cool table frame as she tried to stop the trembling in her arms and legs.

What was that?

Juniper's voice struck her to the core in the silence of the room, "I had to show you what you were missing."

Missing. The word rolled around in her skull with bitter resentment.

"You've been learning about the different magic types. I'm born of the Hetreah. What you experienced was a full breath."

Her mind was racing. She was getting tired of learning new information, new secrets. Anger began to churn in the pit of her stomach, warming her chest, and gritting her teeth. Gripping harder, her knuckles began to scream with the strain as she felt emotion boil up her throat. A feral yell escaped past her teeth until she had no breath left. Until she felt the empty release. Peace chasing after on her inhale. Her breath. Not her breath.

Juniper spoke gently, "You and others before you have experienced this same pain." She began taking small steps towards Imogen, watching her movements.

Others before her. Others before her learning that they had been holding their breath this whole time and that it was still not theirs. That it will never be theirs. Despair crept into Imogen's anger and overflow onto her cheeks. "It's not fair," her voice breaking and ending on a sob.

Easing her way around the glass shards, Juniper stood by Imogen and pulled her into a hug, "I know honey. It wasn't fair for them and it's not fair for you." Imogen sunk into Juniper's embrace and buried her face into her shoulder, letting the tears run their course.

~ PEYTON MARNIE **CRAM**

REFLECTION QUESTIONS FOLLOWING THE PROCESS OF BREATHING

As explained at the conclusion of Process One, these reflection questions are for your own personal study. How you use them is largely up to you. Journaling on them in a conventional sense is an option, or you may choose to share your insights with a trusted friend, sponsor, fellow creative, or even your therapist. In sharing your reflections or even the specific pieces you created in your process, it is important to release the attachment we may have to receiving positive feedback. Ask your sharing partner, instead, what came up for them emotionally or what they related to as you share your work or your responses to these questions.

- Describe your personal experience with this process.
- What did you discover in your practice of this process?
- What did you learn about yourself in the process?
- What did you notice about judgment or self-criticism during the process?
- What role did the multi-modality of the art forms play in discovering what you discovered in your process?
- Which of the skills explored in this process can be applied to your overall trauma recovery or wellness plan?

Process three
DISTRESS TOLERANCE

In the event that you are not already aware of this vital truth of recovery—from addiction (substances or behaviors), trauma/mental health concerns, or all of the above—I have some news for you: Just because you get clean and sober, or just because you decide to work on your trauma, life isn't going to get perfect. Life never will. Stressors will continue to bombard you. If you are living in an environment that is not very healthy, there's a chance you are still being subjected to trauma. And the current state of our world suggests we may all be vulnerable to traumatic injury due to forces outside of our control like natural disasters, violence (emotional or physical) by others, or accidents.

However, there is a critical skill that you can acquire called distress tolerance. Distress tolerance is a term used quite a bit in dialectical behavior therapy and other mindfulness-based and mindfulness-informed therapies. Distress tolerance widens our capacity to be with difficult emotions and body sensations, instead of going on autopilot and stuffing or numbing them. Many of us were effectively trained to go into "stuffing" mode or happened to develop this maladaptive reaction to stress as a way to deal with toxicity in our families of origin. The longer I have been a therapist helping people recover from trauma, the more I am convinced that stuffing or numbing emotions (especially with chemicals) may work as a short-term survival strategy, but in the long run, feeling the emotions we experience is the healthier path.

There's an old saying that *the easiest way out is through*. You may have even heard a sponsor or a counselor share this with you and the saying may even cause you to roll your eyes. "Easier said than done," you may protest. And yes, you have a point. We need to acquire skills and strategies to tolerate the *through* and ride out the pain and other uncomfortable emotions that keep us stuck. Distress tolerance skills not only empower us with this skill set, they give us ample opportunities to practice being with difficult emotions so that we can better handle them whenever they arise in life and along our recovery journey.

Another vital truth of the recovery process is that some of the strategies and treatments that can help us long-term: step work in a 12-step program (especially steps 4 and 5, and steps 8 and 9), or trauma-focused therapies like EMDR therapy, trauma-focused CBT, and Somatic Experiencing® can feel brutal. "Going there," that is, taking that journey to the source of your pain in order to work on it can be the emotional equivalent of going through taxing physical therapy after an accident or injury. Thus, we will work in the distress tolerance process now because the skills acquired here will prepare you to tackle the deeper work to come and the naturally distressing emotions that come along with it.

PRACTICE ONE

CONTAINER VISUALIZATION

Containers come in various shapes and sizes and can hold things we are not quite ready to address. What are some examples of containers that you can think of? A Mason jar? A shelf with a drawer? A piece of Tupperware? A tin? A backpack? In this exercise, choose an image or idea that you can use to safely pack away memories, emotions, body sensations, or anything else that you are not quite ready to deal with on a specific day or during a therapy session. This is *NOT* about stuffing or avoiding, so do not choose a container like a lock box you will seal shut and lock up, throwing the key away in the ocean! Containers are for temporary holding, so choose something that you can open and shut as often as your needs require.

- Pick a representation of a container that works for you. Although many different containers may work for this purpose, try to pick something that has great meaning or significance to you.
- Imagine yourself opening the container and placing whatever you may need to store for now inside it. If you need to make a physical gesture of placing things in the container to help make the exercise more real for you, allow yourself to make those gestures. Remember your container is there to help you to manage the negativity until you are ready to deal with it.

- Close the container. You may also choose to use physical gestures to help you with this process. Notice the experience and any sensations that come up with closing the container. Remember to breathe evenly. What do you notice after breathing with those sensations?
- If you wish, you can give your container a name or a phrase. You can use this to remind you of the container whenever you feel distressed.

MODIFICATION NOTE:

✓ In teaching this exercise to clients, I've heard many say, "I have so many things to hold, no container would ever be big enough." The answer to this is quite simple: Your imagination powers this exercise. If you need to use a shipping crate, a massive storage unit, or visualize an entire train to hold your things for this exercise, do it!

PRACTICE TWO

MAKING A CONTAINER

Using whatever materials are available to you, the next step of the process is to physically make a container. This container can be something that you leave in your living space or office. The container might be something you bring to therapy or to meetings with a sponsor or another guide. You can keep the container open when you are working with your therapist or guide and then close it to signify that your time together is ending and the container now holds whatever emotions might be left over or lingering. If your container is small enough, it may be something that you can carry with you in your bag or keep in your car.

- Shoeboxes and other discarded boxes, jars, or canisters can work well for this process. Craft stores and online retailers sell cardboard, wooden, paper mache, and plastic boxes in a variety of shapes (e.g., circles, squares, ovals, hearts, stars, houses) just waiting to be decorated and designed.
- Consider what kinds of symbols, shapes, images, or colors you would like to put on the outside of your container to strengthen its power. You can use paint, markers, glitter glue, collage materials, scrapbooking pieces, or other items that you have hanging around your living space.
- You can decorate your container as simply or as intricately as you like. Maybe there's a color that carries great meaning for you; creating your

container may be the simple practice of painting a wooden box that color. You may also elect to go into full-on collage mode, expressing on the outside and inside of your container anything that may be helpful to you in holding difficult emotions or sensations until you are ready to work on them again. You can apply a sealant like shellac or *ModPodge®* to the outside of your work when you are finished to keep the pieces you've added from falling off.

- Give yourself plenty of time to let this process unfold. Notice what happens for you as you engage in this practice.
- If the full range of materials is not available to you to make the container you would like, consider drawing your ideal container as an alternative. Remember, this does not have to be a perfect piece of art; rather, it is something that you can access at any time as a visual reminder of your container.

MODIFICATION NOTE:

✓ If you needed to use a large-scale container in your visualization in Practice 1 above, making one in this practice may seem infeasible or impractical. You have the option to make a model-size version of that container. For example, you can make a model train to stand in for the actual train that you used for the visualization.

CONTAINER EXAMPLES

~ DR. JAMIE (PRAGYA) **MARICH**

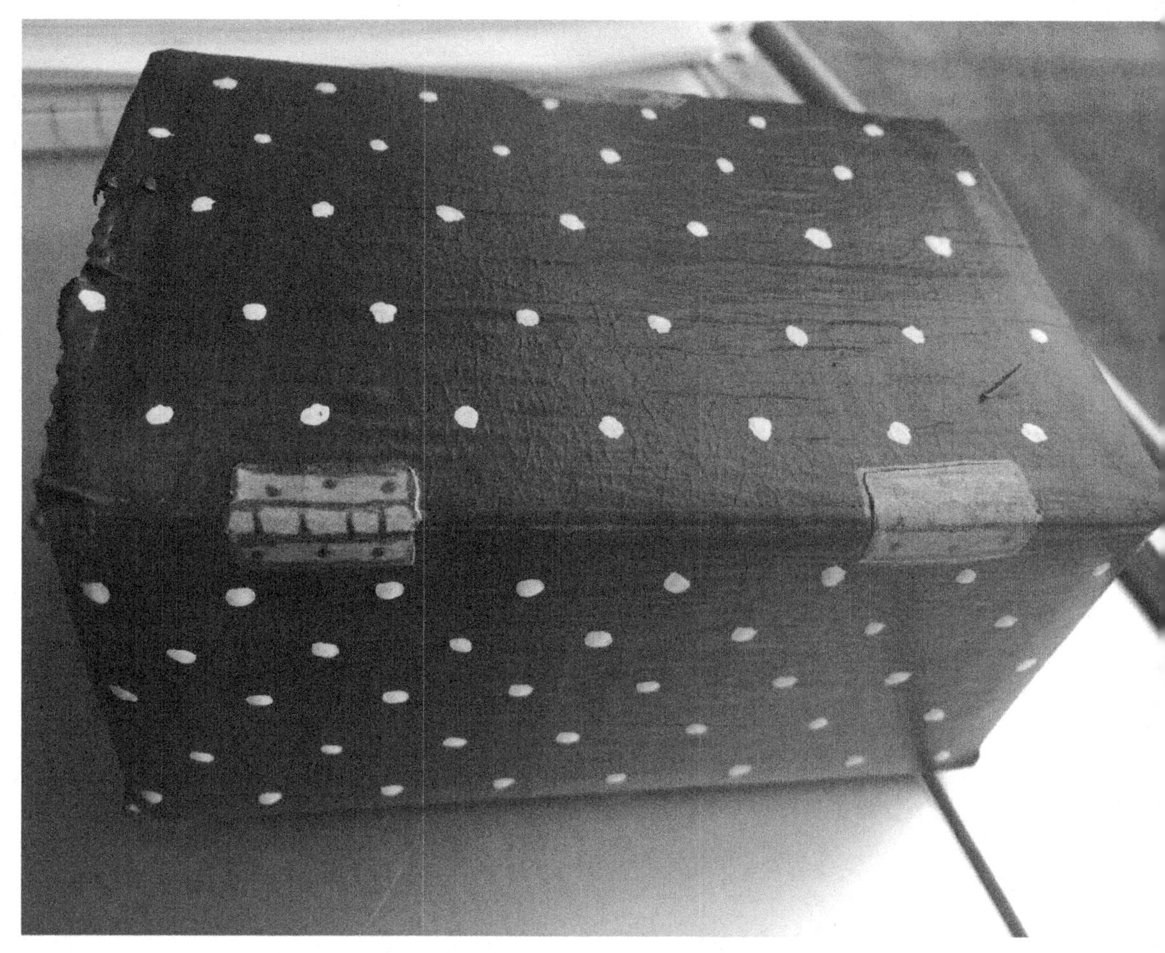

~ ALEXIS RAE **BURROW**

PRACTICE THREE

COMPOSING A PLAYLIST

You are likely familiar with the process of making playlists, especially if you own a smartphone or use YouTube. Even before smartphones, mix tapes and CDs were a way for many to engage in the process of assembling meaningful songs together. I remember clicking PLAY + RECORD while listening to the radio when I was growing up in the 1980s to keep a set of my favorite songs in one place. Even basic mastery of technology in this day and age makes it easy to collect your favorite songs, especially those that may be helpful to your recovery process, in one place. If you don't have a Smartphone to use programs like Spotify, Apple Music, Pandora, or countless others that make gathering music easy, it's relatively simple to make a playlist on YouTube (and yes, there are YouTube videos that show you how to do this). If worse comes to worst, the old school method of getting a cassette tape and clicking PLAY + RECORD when your favorite songs come on the radio is still an option in assembling your own personal playlist.

- What songs are most helpful for you to hear when you are in a state of distress? Take a moment to brainstorm what has worked for you in the past. If you can't think of specific songs, what kinds of instruments or genre/vibe of music is most useful to you when you are in distress? Do certain types of distress warrant different kinds of music for you?

- Take as much time as you need to put a playlist together, noticing what the experience is like for you. Maybe there are several different themes of playlists that you wish to make (e.g., "Happy Songs," "Spiritual Tunes," etc.)
- Put this to the test in real life. Consider listening to one of your playlists before you go to sleep each night or the next time you are pelted with stress—put on one of your playlists and notice what you notice. You have the option of engaging in mindful listening, sitting or lying down as you listen to the playlist, or you may elect to keep the playlist running in your car or put on headphones as you take a walk.

MODIFICATION NOTE:

✓ There is no set length regarding how long a playlist needs to be, so as you start this practice do what works for you. A three-song playlist can be just as effective as a list with 25 songs.

PRACTICE FOUR

LISTEN TO MUSIC YOU DON'T LIKE

Are you a chronic channel changer? When you listen to the radio, or when you have listened to it in the past, and a song comes on you don't like or are not quite feeling, is your tendency to change the channel to find a better song? If you use a music service on your smartphone or computer and your music is set to shuffle, do you do the same thing? In this practice and its variations, your challenge is to practice listening to the songs you don't like or are not quite in the mood for. The challenge is to spend the 3–5 minutes that the song is on to just listen, perhaps using your breath to help you. I cannot think of a better metaphor for practicing distress tolerance in life and in recovery than this: You can't control what life plays on the radio or how life randomly shuffles the music. Distress tolerance requires us, metaphorically speaking, to listen to songs that we don't like or may not be the best fit for us at any given moment. So why not literally use this experience to help us practice the skill of distress tolerance?

- Start small if you wish (this is also the modification note for this practice). Perhaps challenge yourselves to pick a genre of music you don't like, an artist you don't care for, or an instrument that makes your skin crawl a bit. If you have trauma or trigger responses associated with certain styles of music or songs, you do not have to go there with this practice. Just start with something you don't like. After all, life and recovery ask us to do many things that we don't like.

- After you've listened to the first song all the way through you have some options. You can elect to do this listening to "one song I don't like" as a daily practice, just for the 3-5 minutes.
- If you feel up for it and/or want to *really* practice widening your affective window of tolerance, make a whole playlist of songs, instruments, artists, or moods you don't like. This is excellent training for the rigors of deeper therapy and for the tough seasons of recovery.
- You can simply do what is suggested in the opening to this practice. Challenge yourself to listen to the radio continuously for one hour or keep your music set on shuffle for an hour, committing not to change the channel or advance to the next song. Perhaps notice how often you have the tendency to do that. When irritation or discomfort arises, breathe, notice it, and return your attention to listening without judgment.

PRACTICE FIVE

MOVE TO MUSIC YOU DON'T LIKE

In the previous practice, you were invited to listen to a song you don't like; to challenge yourself. You also had the option of making an entire playlist. This practice invites us into the natural blend of music and movement.

- Start by cuing up the original song you listened to in Practice 4.
- Instead of just listening to it, you are now challenged to move to it. This movement can take many shapes: You can dance, walk along to it, stretch, bop along, or just move your hands back and forth.
- In the spirit of non-judgment, notice what happens and what your movement may reveal as you move to the music.
- Remember, you can modify this practice by starting smaller, perhaps moving to just a segment of a song instead of the whole song.
- For optimal challenge, move mindfully to the entire playlist that you created in Practice 4. You may be surprised at what you discover!

PRACTICE SIX

TAKING IT TO THE PAGE

To continue the multi-art exploration and wrap up this process we now move on to writing. There are a variety of places you can go with this writing experience, depending upon your personal needs right now. Honor what your emotions, your body, and your overall experiences are telling you that you most need.

- In this version of *Taking it to the Page*, following the movement practice invite a period of 5–10 minutes of free form journaling. You may consider setting a timer to make sure you keep writing and avoid judging yourself too harshly. Even if what you're writing feels like nonsense, commit to writing for the period of time that you set.
- You may choose to leave this process with the free form journaling or move on to composing another written form like poetry or a short story. Notice what you most need and see what flows naturally.
- After you finish this writing, write or draw on a separate page anything that surfaced during your writing practice that you might need to contain in the moment. This is a perfect opportunity to practice using the container you made. You can write whatever may be lingering for you on a slip of paper and place it in your container. Remember that putting such items in the container is not to avoid them or stuff them away. Rather, what you offer to the container is to be visited later.

MODIFICATION NOTE:

- ✓ For this and any writing practice in this book, you can choose to physically write in a paper journal using a pen or any other color implement, or you can type your writing using a computer or smartphone. Again, I ask you to notice which method is most helpful for you in getting in touch with your feelings and experiences. This may involve trying out different options and deciding from there. As a reminder you have the option to handwrite your work and then enter it into a word processing program later where more connections may reveal themselves.

REFLECTION QUESTIONS FOLLOWING DISTRESS TOLERANCE

- Describe your personal experience with the process of distress tolerance.

- What did you discover in your process?

- What did you learn about yourself in the process?

- What did you notice about judgment or self-criticism during the process?

- What role did the multi-modality of the art forms play in discovering what you discovered in your process?

- Which of the skills explored in this process can be applied to your overall trauma recovery or wellness plan?

Process Four

MINDFULNESS

Mindfulness has gotten a great deal of press in recent years. Twenty-five years ago, most people outside the spheres of Buddhist or yoga communities hadn't even heard of this ancient practice. Now, it seems to be everywhere. In 2014, Time Magazine ran a piece called "The Mindfulness Revolution," complete with a front-page cover featuring a person looking like she was in total bliss. As nice as it is for mindfulness to go mainstream, some of the ways in which it is marketed are problematic. You may have seen that Time Magazine cover (easily available through an online search) or other images of mindfulness and immediately say, "That's not me! There's no way I'll ever be able to be that calm." Indeed, if you do a search engine exploration of the word *mindfulness,* several very clichéd images display. Often you will see a beautiful lotus flower, the pristine ripple on a pond, a rock formation, or a Zen garden with the sand perfectly combed. Or, you may be treated to more images like the Time Magazine cover: perfect looking people sitting in a state of bliss, usually on a beach or underneath a tree somewhere.

Not only do many of my clients and students roll their eyes when they see such imagery, I do too! I've practiced Eastern meditation in various systems for over a decade and I've practiced in contemplative Christian traditions for even longer. And yet, on most days my meditation, prayer, and yoga practices are still a struggle. If someone were to take my picture on any given day when I practice, they'd be more likely to encounter images of frustration and strain on my face. Trust me, I drop F-bombs and other expletives regularly when I stay in the moment with whatever life brings me. Most times I don't like the (insert F-bomb) moment and the reality of living life on life's terms. My practice has taught me to keep noticing without judgment, breathe as I stay grounded, and inevitably, whatever I'm experiencing will pass. Afterwards, when I step off the laboratory of my yoga mat or meditation cushion, I find myself better able to deal with whatever life throws my way.

Mindfulness has been described by many scholars and practitioners as learning how to *respond* instead of react to stress. Mindfulness doesn't make stress go away, rather, it teaches us how to better manage it or to roll with it. A common metaphor attributed to Jon Kabat-Zinn is that you *can't stop the waves from coming, but you can learn how to surf.* Another variation on this age-old idea is encapsulated in the wisdom: *Life isn't about waiting for the storm to pass; it's about learning how to dance in the rain*. When you are suffering, these meme-worthy sayings may seem beyond your capacity to actualize. However, through practice and time, my lived experience has taught me that they are very true. They speak to the essence of how deliberately practicing returning to the present while not pushing away our experiences of the moment can serve us in recovery and in life.

A major part of practicing mindfulness that we will explore fully in this process is to not judge yourself if you feel that you are failing at it. Yes, the process affords you several practices for learning to live in the moment, practices that are both traditional and more expressive. If you catch your attention wandering, simply bring your attention back to your intended point of focus. One of my favorite working definitions of mindfulness is drawn from the Sanskrit teaching and translation of the word—*the practice of coming back to awareness*. Awareness is our natural state, although we live in a world where we are constantly pulled away from awareness of the present moment. Moreover, our self-criticisms and judgments can keep us out of the experience of living a life of awareness and consciousness.

So, if your protest going into this process is something like, "I can't be mindful, I can't sit still," congratulations! You are in good company. Because, on many days I can't sit still either. And when I first began studying mindfulness and yoga in earnest, it was even more of a struggle. I am not impressed if you can sit still for 25 minutes in perfect harmony with your breath. What I do honor is your willingness to approach each of the following practices with a sense of curiosity and openness. Know that even if your head wanders away from the practice ten times a minute, at any given time you have the power to return home to focus on the moment. Working on and developing this skill will serve you well as you enter into the deeper stages of your healing to follow.

PRACTICE ONE

DEEPENING THE BREATH WITH MINDFUL INTENTION

If you want to study mindful breathing with a perfect teacher, find an infant and watch them breathe. Babies naturally breathe with their bellies. Somewhere along the way as we grow up and become less mindful, this tendency to breathe with our natural state of awareness gets lost. Rapid, shallow breathing that originates in the chest can become the norm. In this practice, you are invited to explore the foundational breath of yoga: diaphragmatic breathing, sometimes called *belly breathing*. As with all elements of mindful breathing, belly breathing takes practice. If you tend to self-criticize for not "doing it right," simply invite your breath pattern back to what seems like any natural beginning place. As the Catholic mystic St. Benedict taught (congruent with the Buddhist idea of beginner's mind), *always we can begin again.* Here are some basic steps to begin the practice:

- Come into a comfortably seated position that you can sustain for the next few minutes. While you have the option to lie down, try the practice in a sitting position first.
- Put one or both hands on the upper area of your stomach so that you can pay attention to the motion of your diaphragm.
- As you inhale with your nose, allow your belly to expand outward as far as it will go.

- Exhale with your mouth, allowing the belly to pull back in.
- Continue this inhale-exhale pattern at your own pace, giving it at least 6-7 repetitions (about one minute) to find a rhythm and style that work for you.

MODIFICATION NOTES:

✓ Start small—if the suggested number of repetitions/time length seems too overwhelming, begin with just one full breath, reevaluate, and then decide if you wish to continue with additional repetitions.

✓ If you feel awkward or in any way out of control with the suggested pattern, consider starting with an exhale instead of an inhale.

✓ After initially experimenting with the breath and finding the rhythm that works for you, considering puckering the mouth slightly, and exhaling as if you are blowing through a straw. For some people, the mouth pucker, combined with a longer exhale, enhances their experience of relaxation.

✓ If paying attention to the breath on its own is not working for you, consider adding a count to it (e.g., In "1" Out "1," In "2" Out "2," and continue until you get to 10, and then start again at 1). Using numbers as an anchor can help you stay focused on the task at hand: breathing. You can also add a word or a special phrase (e.g., "*Satnam*," "Amen," "Help me," "As I breathe in, I know I am breathing in; as I breathe out, I know I am breathing out").

✓ You can put something like a Beanie Baby or a flatter type of stuffed animal on your stomach so there is a focus point while you observe the rise and fall of the belly. This works especially well if you want to try the practice lying down.

✓ If watching the video instructions would be helpful to you, a supplementary teaching is available at **www.traumamadesimple.com/pnp**

PRACTICE TWO

BREATHE WITH EXPRESSION

The classic breath techniques in yoga and other Eastern approaches to meditation begin with an inhale through the nose to allow for maximum benefit and flow of the breath. While many teachers and clinicians get into the conventional directive to "Inhale with the nose and exhale through the mouth," there is a great deal of liberty with how you can expel the breath. In essence, the inhalation is standard (in through the nose as you expand the belly) while the exhalation affords us many options for expression! In this practice I will cover several yogic breath techniques aside from diaphragmatic breathing. However, practicing diaphragmatic breath first provides a solid foundation for deriving optimal benefit from this experience.

The modification notes for Practice 2 are written into the instructions for each specific type of breathing.

UJJAYI BREATH (OCEAN BREATHING OR "DARTH VADER" BREATHING)

- Pucker your mouth like you're sucking through a straw or about to kiss someone. Attempt to contract the back of your throat so it feels slightly closed.
- Inhale with your nose; your belly ought to expand with this motion.
- Exhale with your nose. Try to keep the mouth closed and let the nose make the exhale.

- If your mouth is puckered and throat constricted, you ought to hear what sounds like the ocean within you.
- Attempt to keep your inhales and exhales even, especially while you're first learning this breath. Do not try more than five full repetitions during your first attempt. Starting slowly can be a valuable modification with all the breaths that have therapeutic benefit, and it's especially important with this very dynamic breath.
- It is completely normal if you feel somewhat light headed, but it should be a "good" light-headed. If it does not feel good, chances are you tried too many too soon, or your inhales and exhales were uneven.
- You can envision different characters with this breath, like Darth Vader, or a charging bull "huffing and puffing." Be open to whatever movie references or other creative anchors may come up for you.
- Get a mirror and see the steam of your breath on the surface (young people like this especially), attuning you to the idea of your breath as "the Force."
- You can visualize (on any breath) that you are breathing in a calming or soothing color and breathing out a color that represents stress. John Coffey from the movie *The Green Mile* is another favorite character that I like to intone when I do *ujjayi* breath with expression. In the film, every time he healed someone, he would raise his head and exhale (with sound) the pestilence or disease that he just took from the person he healed.
- If watching the video instructions would be helpful to you, supplementary teachings are available at **www.traumamadesimple.com/pnp**

LION BREATHING

- Begin with a healthy inhale from the belly.
- Exhale vigorously, allowing the tongue to hang out. Feel the jaw and cheeks loosen. Open the eyes widely to help with this letting go. With your hands, make paws like a lion to complete the effect of a lion roaring.
- Try at least 5 full repetitions, although if one full breath is all you can manage at first that is okay.
- Consider how embodying the strength of a lion or enrolling in the character of a lion can help you breathe through a painful trigger with strength and confidence. For professionals, bringing in other expressive arts elements, like using a costume or acting out a scene, may help your client further develop the breath as a resource.
- If watching the video instructions would be helpful to you, a supplementary teaching is available at **www.traumamadesimple.com/pnp**

BREATHING OUT THE DRAMA OR "SIGH OF RELIEF"

- The lion paws are a fun element well known to many practitioners, although how you express your arms and face when you exhale vigorously is completely up to you.
- On this next round of breathing, continue by inhaling with the nose and expanding the belly like usual.
- Allow the expressions your body and your face makes on the exhale to flow out naturally, making a sound if possible.
- Many people describe this breath as the "sigh of relief" or being "dramatic" on their exhale. While you can use these examples if they work for you, don't let them limit you in keeping an open mind and open heart to what the practice can reveal!

PRACTICE THREE

MINDFUL COLORING

These practices are combined because part of my intention is for you to notice the similarities and the differences in creating through each form. What can having more containment and direction teach you about mindfulness and expression? What can the absence of containment and direction teach you about mindfulness and expression? These practices are designed to help you explore such questions. You are encouraged to set aside enough time to do both of these practices in the same sitting.

- The *adult coloring book movement* has become very popular as a stress relief activity in recent years. In this practice you are simply invited to color a page, either from a specialized book that you own, a source you find online (search "coloring pages" and millions will come up), or using a children's coloring book. I've also provided three sample images (in the following pages) that you can use if you don't have access to your own.
- You are encouraged to explore how engagement with coloring may help you to connect mindfully, especially with concentrated breath.
- Consider how such an exercise can be utilized as a containment strategy before moving into the more free-form gush art.

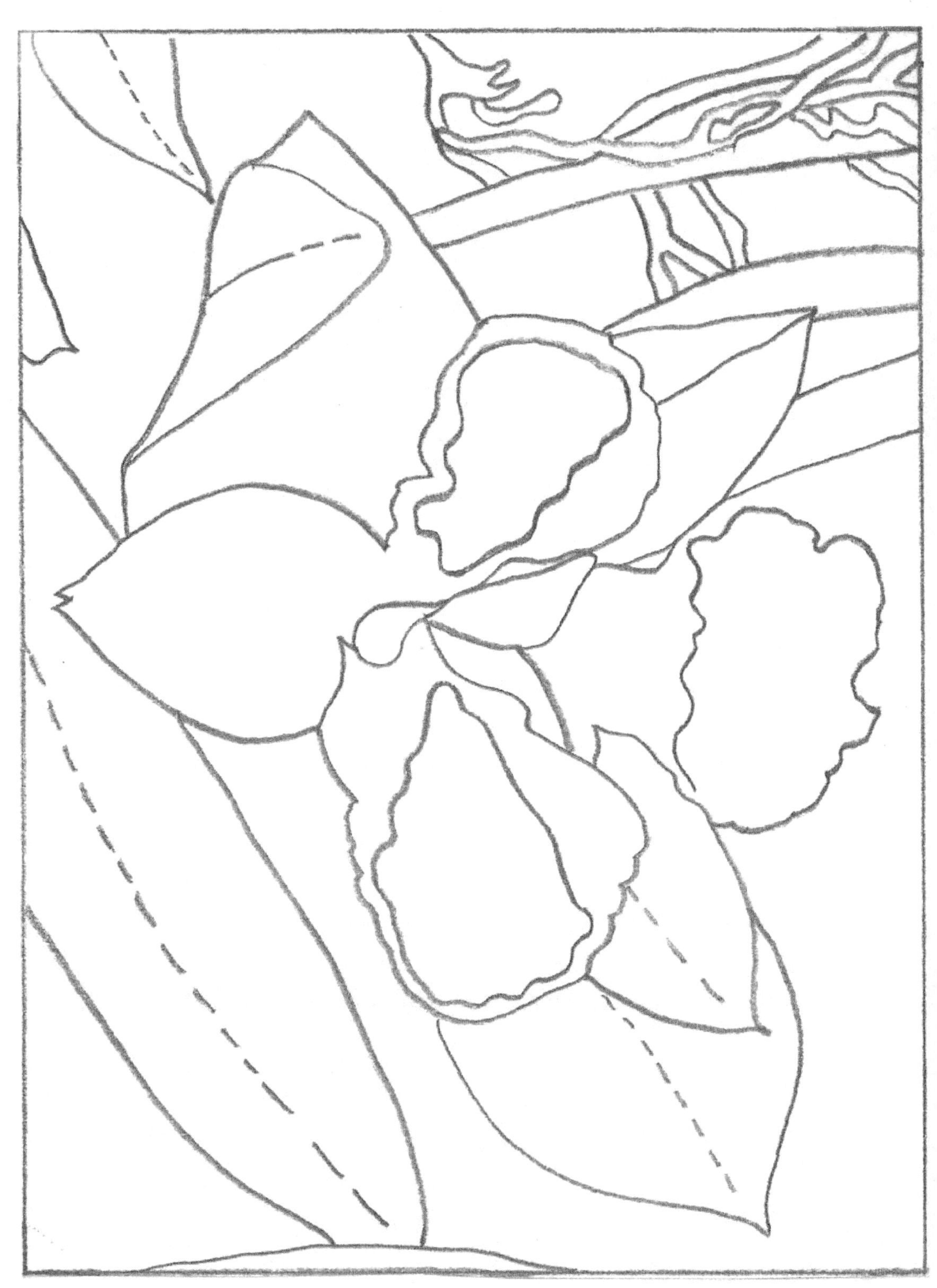

Coloring Page by ~ KATIE **GIFFORD**

Coloring Page by ~ KATIE **GIFFORD**

Coloring Page by ~ KATIE **GIFFORD**

PRACTICE FOUR

GUSH ART

As noted earlier, gush art is a term used in expressive arts therapy to suggest uncensored creation with art—think of what the word "gush" means for you and allow that to unfold on the page using the materials you have available to you (e.g., crayons, markers, pastels, paints, etc.). Gush art was a part of Process One: Grounding. You are encouraged to release that experience and focus on this new experience of gush art and notice what it reveals for you, especially after Mindful Coloring.

- Like with many forms of meditation, it can be useful to set a timer for the gush art practice. This helps keep the focus on the process of the experience. When the timer expires, check in and notice whatever it is you notice about the experience and/or move along to the next practice.
- Set a timer for gush art (10–15 minutes) to avoid being pulled in to overthinking or being fixated on the outcome.

GUSH ART EXAMPLES

~ JENNIFER **HARWOOD**

~ TRACEE **MOSS**

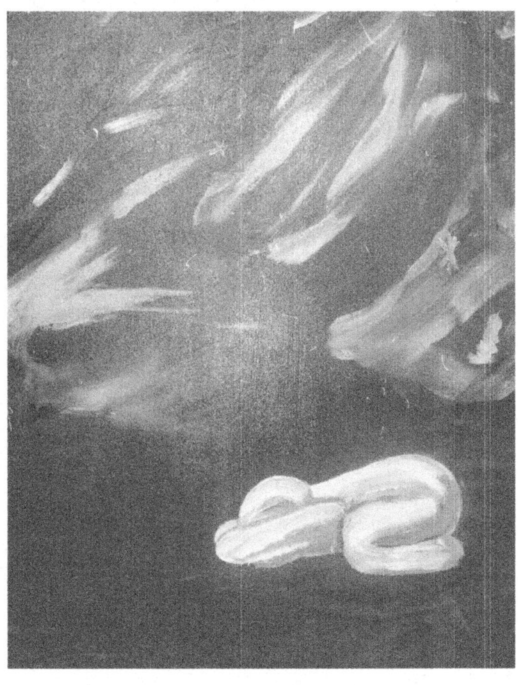

~ PEYTON MARNIE **CRAM**

~ KAMALA **TAHYI**

PRACTICE FIVE

EMBRACE-RELEASE-EMBRACE

We can embrace the moment, embrace an emotion we are experiencing (whether it be challenging or pleasant), or embrace the pesky thoughts that pass through our rational mind. In this mindful movement practice, we work with the idea of learning to embrace whatever life brings. All mindfulness practice and indeed all of life is a process of learning to embrace (instead of resist or shove away) whatever may come, then learning how to let go of what we can and need to at any given moment. This movement practice will give you a chance to explore this natural flow.

- Come into a gesture of embracing yourself, if this works for you today. You know, the good old "give yourself a hug" posture. Moving consciously while giving yourself this hug may allow you to embrace whatever the moment is sending your way. Sometimes what surfaces in the moment is challenging to embrace. Often this challenge is dancing with experience from the past or an old story about self that keeps us stuck in a proverbial rut.
- You have a choice with this practice. You can use the posture of embrace to physically support the practice of noticing and receiving the moment without judgment, or explore whether the dance allows you to loosen the embrace and release the arms freely.

- If you choose to let go of whatever you've been embracing, you can allow the universe, Mother Earth, the God of your understanding, or whatever seems organic to you in that moment to take that which you are letting go. Can you allow the process of letting go to transform what you are releasing into something beautiful? In the next moments of dance or perhaps during some other practice when you feel ready, embrace the transformations fully and without apology.
- If the metaphor of this practice seems too much to start with, simply work with the gesture pattern of embracing-releasing-embracing, putting on whatever music you prefer for the practice. Notice whatever it is you may notice and consider going to one of your other art forms to help you process whatever this movement practice may conjure up for you, or to hold the emotion of this practice in containment until you can consult with your therapist or a trusted support figure.

MODIFICATION NOTES:

✓ This practice can be done in silence or with music. You may consider starting with silence to get the flow of the embrace-release-embrace pattern, and then putting on music of your choosing.

✓ If watching the video instructions would be helpful to you, a supplementary teaching is available at **www.traumamadesimple.com/pnp**

PRACTICE SIX

TAKE IT TO THE PAGE (WRITTEN DIALOGUE EXPLORATION)

This process concludes with a written exploration that will hopefully help you to crystallize your experience. For this practice in taking it to the page, you will need to have your coloring page and your gush art handy. Take a few moments to breathe and sink into the moment before you begin.

- Take about 2 minutes to fully observe the page you colored. This is an exercise in observation, not judgment or scrutiny. Notice which element of the colored page most catches your attention. Maybe it's one petal of one flower. Perhaps it's the color blue. It could even be the white space around what you colored.
- Set your timer for 5 minutes. On a blank page or in your journal, spend the time writing *as* the element you just noticed. In expressive arts practices, this exercise commonly uses the lead-in: "I am (e.g., the color blue), I . . . " Allow your free writing to flow from there. If you need more inspiration, think about the message that the element (like the color blue) may have for you today and write from that place.
- After the timer rings, put your pen or writing implement down and then take a minute to breathe and reset.

- Now take about 2 minutes to fully observe your gush art. Remember, this is an exercise in observation, not judgment or scrutiny. Notice which element of the gush art catches your attention most.
- Set your timer for 5 minutes. On a blank page or in your journal, spend the time writing *as* the element you just noticed. You can also use the lead-in "I am (e.g., the color blue), I am the one who . . . " for this part of the practice.
- After the time rings, put your pen or writing implement down and then take a minute to breathe and reset.
- For the final portion of this practice, you are invited to set the timer for 10 minutes and allow the two elements—the one from the coloring page and the one from the gush art—to interact with each other. You can write a short scene like a play, a poem, a short story, or any other presentation of the written word that makes sense to you.

MODIFICATION NOTE:

✓ In trauma-focused practice, the amount of time that you spend in a practice is always variable. If the parameters presented in this set up feel too long for you, consider shortening them. I've seen people do great things with this exercise writing for only 1-2 minutes in each portion.

GUSH ART AND WRITING RESPONSE EXAMPLE

I am water in the ocean
that creates a wave that is
intense, forceful & fierce.
I have the ability to soothe, to
provide fun, to carry, to be gentle –
and the capability to destroy,
to drown, to injure, to ruin, to
damage, to suffocate, &
to choke
It all depends on the conditions
in my environment that dictate
the waves created.
What will I produce next?

I am a seed
that is often buried
Invisible, laying in the
dark
The seed I am becomes
something more; a flower,
food, vegetables, grassy earth.
How exciting to know what
I, a seed, will become
once the darkness fades.

Seed: I know! I stand so tall &
strong – I have you to thank; for
without your care, guidance, and
reliability; I would not have thrived.

Water: Even though you are fully bloomed; I am by your side
to continue to nourish; during
your whole life cycle; I will always
provide.

(Hand in hand; flower and water sat in the sun talked, laughed
and "allowed each other to just be")

~ TRACEE **MOSS**

REFLECTION QUESTIONS FOLLOWING MINDFULNESS

- Describe your personal experience with the process.
-
- What did you discover in your process?
-
- What did you learn about yourself in the process?
- What did you notice about judgment or self-criticism during the process?
- What role did the multi-modality of the art forms play in discovering what you discovered in your process?
- Which of the skills explored in this process can be applied to your overall trauma recovery or wellness plan?

Process five
SELF COMPASSION

Self-compassion is becoming just as big of a buzzword as mindfulness, especially in wellness and recovery circles. Kristen Neff, Ph.D., is one of the major names associated with the mindful self-compassion movement. The essential message of her landmark book *Self-Compassion: The Proven Power of Being Kind to Yourself* (2015) is: Stop beating yourself up and show yourself the kindness that you might offer more freely to someone you love. In this process, we will explore what being kind to yourself truly means, especially as it relates to trauma and recovery.

If you come from a 12-step recovery background, it's possible that doing countless inventories and other exercises that were originally designed to be helpful have left you with a greater sense of shame. You likely learned to ask the classic recovery question, "What's my part in this?" However, sometimes you truly had no part in challenges that you have experienced—there was nothing you did to contribute to what happened. This is reality in cases of trauma, neglect, and abuse.

This process may be especially useful for you as Section I, PREPARING, draws to a close and we begin the transition to Section II, DEEPENING. While the 12 steps and certain faith-based programs of recovery can be extremely useful, I've seen many people engaged in these recovery paths struggle when going deeper with trauma work. To be clear, asking questions like "What's my part in this?" and engaging in other self-inventory angles can help us to build our conscience and develop healthy discernment in our decision making. Often we genuinely played a part in situations and in causing harm to others, and owning this can be beneficial to recovery and to growth. However, if we're beating ourselves up and living in a quagmire of shame, our healing journey may be stifled unless we learn to get unstuck.

Self-compassion practices can help us explore what it means to be kind to ourselves, and they are the focus of this process. One way you can take the extra step in practicing self-compassion as you engage in this process is to know when you may need to step away and seek support. Sometimes encountering the source of our shame can feel overwhelming (shame will get more attention as we journey deeper in to the book). Other times, practicing self-compassion becomes a struggle when you must take responsibility for harm done to others.

After all, this process does not endorse an anything goes, *do whatever you want to whomever you want* approach to life. Rather, how can you work on taking responsibility when and where appropriate yet not get sucked into a vortex of shame? For the time being, practicing mindfulness and noticing what comes up when you explore these practices and their challenges, may prove to be some of the most significant healing work that you've done.

PRACTICE ONE

NOURISHMENT AND DEPLETION INVENTORY

For the first practice in this process, you are invited to try a new type of inventory. You may be familiar with doing inventories in the style of a 12-step program, or by making a list of goals and resolutions. These goals and resolutions can seem like they have positive intent. However, creating this type of list comes with the risk of emphasizing your deficits and pieces of evidence that feed false beliefs such as, "I'm not complete as I am," or "I'm not good enough and have to change." Dr. Christine Valters Paintner taught me the following form of inventory on retreat several years ago. For me, this practice offers us a much kinder way to take stock.

- Spend a minute or two in mindful breathing. Consider setting an intention to allow yourself to write freely without censoring yourself or judging your experience. No one has to see this inventory besides you.
- Take out a piece of paper or go to a blank page in your journal. Make a line down the middle to create two columns on the page. Or, if you are using a journal or notebook, you can use two pages that face each other.
- On the left side column (or page), take about 5 minutes to write down the people, places, things, and activities in your life that nourish you. If the word nourish is tricky for you, look it up in the dictionary for some additional inspiration. My general working definition of nourishment

is to be fed—physically, emotionally, and spiritually—with little or no rebound experienced in the way of negative consequences.

- On the right side, take the next 5 minutes to write down the people, places, things, and activities in your life that deplete you. Be mindful that some of the same people, places, things, and activities may appear in both columns. This often happens when you list children or close family members. It is more than okay to have something, someone, or someplace appear on both columns or pages. If that happens, try to be more specific about what aspects of these entities are nourishing for you and what aspects are depleting.
- When you are done, give yourself a few minutes to breathe and center yourself before looking over your list. Do any surprises or new discoveries show up when you review your inventory?

MODIFICATION NOTES:

✓ If you are concerned about someone you live with or who is in your close space finding this inventory (especially if they appear on it), know that you can destroy it as soon as you compose and review it. You can run it through a shredder, burn it, or tear it up into little pieces and flush it down the toilet. The important part is that you set an intention to internalize what you discovered in the exercise before moving on with this process.

✓ If you struggle with verbalizing words on a page, drawing in symbols or images is also permissible, although the next practice will take you into fuller exploration with visual components.

✓ **BONUS PRACTICE:** If one of the items on your nourishing list is an expressive arts practice, consider carving out some time today or in the coming days to spend a solid chunk of time engaging in that practice.

PRACTICE TWO

COLLAGE MAKING

Now, you are invited to shift into bringing images to your inventory. Collage making is the practice of taking images gathered from a variety of sources, like old magazines, old photographs, and other scrap material, and bringing them together into a whole. If you don't have easy access to magazines, you can also print images from the Internet, although be advised that local libraries and medical offices are typically very willing to get rid of old magazines.

- You can make two separate collages or divide one large piece of foundational paper into two sides.
- On your first collage or on the left side of your paper, make a collage that displays images of what you find depleting. If you are hesitant to put a specific image of a person into this collage, think of another image you can use that represents what specifically about that person and your relationship with them depletes you.
- On your second collage or on the right side of your paper, make a collage that displays images of what you find nourishing. The same guidance applies if you prefer not to use actual images of people. Find images of what they represent to you.
- In making your collage, release any hang-ups you may have about making them look perfect. Collages are perfect for working with messy

and disparate pieces that may not seem like they go together. Do not force or strive in this practice; just see what unfolds organically as you begin playing with images.

- When you are done, give yourself a few minutes to breathe and center before looking over your collage inventory. What are the images showing you? What are you noticing in your body as you take in the visuals?

MODIFICATION NOTES:

- ✓ While images and collages may seem less scary than leaving written words hanging around, you also have the right to destroy these pieces when you are done, especially if you live in an environment where you don't feel optimally safe. Before destroying your work or asking someone else to hold it for safekeeping, make a solid intention to internalize what you discovered in this practice before moving on with the process.
- ✓ If collage materials are not available to you, gush art and drawing images are good alternative approaches for this exercise. However, since gush art has already been explored in two other processes, you are encouraged to try something new.

COLLAGE MAKING EXAMPLES

~ ALEXIS RAE **BURROW**

~ KAMALA **TAHYI**

"Sometimes the hardest thing to wear is your own skin."
Current Faves
Tracee Moss
Visual Resources:
You like to think you're never wrong
You want someone to hurt like you
"You never had a soul so you preyed upon mine." ~Tracee

~ TRACEE **MOSS**

PRACTICE THREE

LISTENING TO THE MOVEMENTS

In the previous practice the final reflection question asks you: What are you noticing in your body as you take in the visual(s)? This practice invites you to take that body wisdom a step further. The body will speak to you if you are willing to listen.

- Look at the collage that represents depletion for you once again. What are you noticing your body as you take in the visual?
- Express what you are feeling with a gesture, a movement, or by bringing your body into a certain shape. Remember that facial expressions can be a part of this practice component.
- Now, look at the collage that represents nourishment for you. What are you noticing in your body as you take in this visual?
- Express what you are feeling with a gesture, a facial expression, a movement, or by bringing your body into a certain shape.
- Take a moment to pause and give yourself a few breaths to rest.
- For the next part of the practice, you are invited to first make the depletion expression with your body, and then make the nourishment expression with your body. Continue this sequence, making it into a free flow—going back and forth between the expressions.

- You do not have to stay rigid. Let your breath guide you and notice what begins to happen or unfold as you engage with the interplay between the two expressions.
- Stay in this practice for at least 5 minutes.
- When complete, take a moment to breathe into the sensations generated in your body. Notice the stillness after the movement.

MODIFICATION NOTES:

✓ If 5 minutes feels like too much for this first go, shorten the amount of time you spend in the practice. Try to give yourself at least a minute, or 3 repetitions of each expression.

✓ If standing up to move is not available to you right now, you can do this practice sitting or even lying down.

✓ You may elect to use music for this practice. If so, choose a piece that does not have lyrics so that you can deeply listen to what the body is saying. Lyrics may interfere with this experience.

PRACTICE FOUR

TAKE IT TO THE PAGE (FREE WRITING)

This next practice is simple, though not easy. Take out a piece of paper or go to a blank page in your journal and write freely on what the movements in Practice 3 revealed to you. Keep your collages handy for reference if needed, although the focus of this practice is putting into words what you learned by *listening to your movements.*

- Setting a timer may help you with overthinking your experience or focusing too much on outcome. 5 minutes is recommended for this practice.
- You are encouraged not to write in complete sentences or to even use coherent grammar. If run-on sentences come up for you naturally, go with them. If sentence fragments come up for you naturally, go with them.
- If, as you are writing, an inner critic emerges about not writing correctly, thank them for their opinion—and let their opinion go with your next exhale. Be loud about that exhale if you need to.

MODIFICATION NOTE:

- ✓ If writing is not accessible to you at the moment due to an impairment or injury, consider recording your free flow reflections. If you trust someone in your support group to write down what comes up for you naturally, that's an option as well.

TAKE IT TO THE PAGE EXAMPLES

Journey

Do you see that light?
Do you see it now?
Lift your head.
Open your eyes.
It's your hope
in the blackest of nights.
Do you see the light?
Do you see it now?
Nourishing the seeds
sowed into your soul.
Rooting and reaching.
What bout now?
Can you see it now?
The warmth blossoming in your heart.
It's okay.
Take their hand.
Do you see it now?
What you thought were prison walls
is your skin. Your body.
Those scars are your story.
Do you see it now?
Your flame. Your hope. Your love.
You. You. You.
Can you see you?
That is you beckoning you home.

~ PEYTON MARNIE **CRAM**

Go Dark

It's dark and scary going to the silence.
The silence has so much to say
when silence is not honored.
It's a shadow of hidden aspects
to myself. Mindfulness wants
me to be present, to notice &
to observe. The silence calls
awareness to my body. I
don't like feeling my skin my
breath, my stomach, I don't
like noticing my shell – it's
painful. The silence wants
to remind me. Mindfulness
wants to accept me. Each
time though, I cringe – I
want to separate from this
body; only leave my soul-
that at which I know is
beautiful and free and
loving. Maybe that is why I chose to have stylish
clothes, hair & makeup?

To match the inner beauty
with the outer shell? I don't
like feelings the outer shell &
mindfulness blasts the
spotlight on it all. Movement
makes me feel so dirty &
gross. The silence does too.
Will I ever reach a place
where loving my body will
set me free? Will I ever be
free of shame in this area?
Mindfulness, please help
me; silence please be forgiving.
Everyone, everything, & Tracee,
you are not your skin. Let
your soul, you light, and
your beauty shine out &
be the forefront for the
rest of this life. Then, you
shall be free.
Quiet
Be still

~ TRACEE **MOSS**

PRACTICE FIVE

THE POEM OF INSTRUCTION

Again, I give the credit to my expressive arts mentor, Christine Valters Paintner, for teaching me this practice, which I've modified to fit into the flow of our process on self-compassion. The Poem of Instruction is, as the name suggests, a series of lines that will serve as directions or instructions for how you will take care of yourself; specifically how you will practice self-compassion moving forward with this work. Remember that what makes poetry *poetry* is that you decide where the lines begin and end, and you determine how long or short they will be.

- Consult your free writing from the previous practices and your collage pieces to prepare for writing your poem.
- What have the practices in this process taught you thus far about mindful self-compassion? Use your answer to this question to form these lessons into a poem of instruction, which you can simply approach as a list of invitations for you to follow on a daily or regular basis.
- The list does not have to be long, so make it organic for you. Consider approaching this poem as a reminder for yourself that you can access whenever you need it. You can keep this poem in your journal or copy/type a version of it so it is accessible to you in places where you are likely to see it.

MODIFICATION NOTES:

- ✓ Visit some of the sample Poems of Instruction on the following pages if you need inspiration, although try not to let this sway your personal experience.
- ✓ Remember that the length is variable. Some of the best poems out there are just 1-2 lines long.

POEMS OF INSTRUCTION EXAMPLES

Toward Embodiment

(Written in a Yoga Studio)

The body is the doorway
to the now—go to it.
Learn to knock on it
and see if something comes
to greet you.
Maybe you hear blinds close,
feet scurry to safety.
Knock again, it's okay—
this is your home.
Place your hands on the knob—
turn it on purpose.
Feel the pressure of the door
against your hands—
that pressure is you too.
Peek into the foyer
of the now—see what it holds.
Stand there a minute.
Notice how it opens to everything.

~ THOMAS **ZIMMERMAN**

Chaos

Never forget
In the midst of
anger
pain
rage
despair
hopelessness
fear
grief
regret
shame
guilt
There are seeds
of healing
beauty
peace
gratitude
hope
joy
connection
Destruction and creation are the same energies

~ RAMONA **SKRIIKO**

PRACTICE SIX

RECORDING YOUR SPOKEN WORD

One of the most frightening prospects for all of us, even those of us who speak for a living, is to hear our voice recorded back to us! We tend to instantly go into self-criticism mode about how shrill we sound, how dumb we sound, how many times we say "um" or stutter, and the list goes on. In this practice, you are invited to directly address this fear and use it as a chance to practice being kind to yourself.

- Get out your smartphone, your computer, or a standard tape recorder/ other recording device.
- Speak your *Poem of Instruction* into the recorder. Although you may take on more of a performance mode if you wish, you do not have to. Simply reading the poem slowly and guided by breath will suffice.
- After you finish recording, take a moment to pause, breathe, and let yourself reset.
- When you are ready, listen back to the recording. If you notice judgment or self-criticism come up, see if you can let that criticism go the next time that you exhale.
- Now that you've sent the criticism on its way, listen again. This time, listen for what you like about your voice and about the poem you are sharing. You may be surprised by what you discover.

- Use any of the practices you've developed so far in this journey to help you reflect on this experience or to contain and reground if you are feeling a bit vulnerable after sharing your work in this way.

MODIFICATION NOTE:

✓ If you do not have a recording device of any kind, see if a trusted friend or member of your support group would be willing to have you read your poem for them. Remember to do it at least twice: once to get the self-criticism out of the way, and the second time to focus on the beauty in your voice and in your poem.

REFLECTION QUESTIONS FOLLOWING SELF COMPASSION

- Describe your personal experience with the process.
- What did you discover in your process?
- What did you learn about yourself in the process?
- What did you notice about judgment or self-criticism during the process?
- What role did the multi-modality of the art forms play in discovering what you discovered in your process?
- Which of the skills explored in this process can be applied to your overall trauma recovery or wellness plan?

Section 2:
DEEPENING

Process six

EMBODIMENT

There is increasing awareness around the impacts of unhealed trauma on the body. Just look at the titles of some classic books in the helping professions on trauma:

- *The Body Keeps the Score* (Bessel van der Kolk)
- *The Body Never Lies* (Alice Miller)
- *The Body Bears the Burden* (Robert Scaer)
- *The Body Remembers* (Babette Rothschild)
- *Trauma and the Body* (Pat Ogden)

An underlying assumption in each of these books is a truth that I embrace as your guide for *Process Not Perfection:* if traumas remain unhealed or unprocessed, your body will let you know! That trembling you get in your stomach, that tendency to spike your shoulders up toward your ears, the "shut down" effect that can feel like zoning out or drifting off when you need to be paying attention are all potential signs of this phenomenon.

The specific ways unhealed trauma shows up in the body will vary from person to person. The reason your rational brain won't be able to talk it out or reason through it when you are triggered or activated is clear. Unprocessed trauma primarily lives in the lower and more primitive parts of your brain—the limbic brain and the brainstem or R-complex brain. These are the parts of your brain that went into alarm or "shut down" mode to keep you safe at the time a traumatic experience occurred. They were not designed to hold memories and experiences long term. The limbic brain and the R-complex brain have everything to do with the body, emotions, and learning, and almost nothing to do with rational thinking and words. This is why you might be able to talk about what happened to you, and yet your body feels so cut off from the experience. Or the body may just seem to let you down for no apparent reason, especially when you are jolted by something that is even loosely related to your unhealed trauma and its related associations.

To fully experience trauma recovery, people must learn to befriend their bodies. Learning to notice those subtle cues, sensations, and warning signs that something is wrong is a vital skill, as is learning how to soothe the body in the healthiest possible ways. For the deeper levels of healing we explore in this section of our journey, learning to feel what you stuffed or were not able to feel at the time of your traumatic experience(s) is a vital part of the healing process. This may feel new, scary, or even impossible to many of you. Remember that the processes you worked through and skills you developed in the first section of this book are designed to orient you to this process. If, at any time, the work in this section feels overwhelming, those skills will also provide you with the ability to pause if you need to or make a healthy transition back to the activities of your daily life.

I am not asking you to re-experience or to re-live your trauma, although some of the processes and practices in this section may take you back there on some level. Know that the intention is not to flood you or suck you back into the experience, and if you ever sense that you are getting too flooded, use the pause and rest strategies that you developed in the first section, PREPARING. The objective of these processes is to help you express what never had a chance to be expressed when you were wounded—and there are a wide variety of ways to express these feelings, thoughts, and sensations. The whole spirit of the expressive arts path and its variety of options for expression will serve you well here.

The process of embodiment begins this new section on DEEPENING because it provides the ideal transition between the work of preparation and going deeper. Embodiment is essential, and we started to explore it in the first section. However, if you are still experiencing any major blocks around embodiment or impediments to more fully allowing your body to help you with your emotional work, now is an excellent opportunity to clear some of those barriers.

There are many practices that can help us become more embodied. Yoga, meditation, receiving bodywork and energy work, and dance helped me to make the early shifts I needed in my own trauma work and they continue to be vital to my daily growth. Other practices like aerial yoga, jiu-jitsu, and boxing challenged me to explore and move past my edge, teaching me lessons about my body that could never be learned in a classroom or therapy. What I offer you in this process is a sampling of some practices that can get you started with embodiment. Know that there is a vast world to explore for expanding your experience of embodiment outside the scope of this book. We will review some additional options in the third section of our journey, MANIFESTING.

PRACTICE ONE

THE BRAIN-BODY RELATIONSHIP (COLORING ACTIVITY)

We explored the value of coloring pages for honing mindful attention in a previous process. Now, you are invited to work with another coloring page to help orient you to the workings of your brain. I developed this skill in collaboration with Ramona Skriiko, a licensed professional counselor and senior faculty member in my group's expressive arts program. As professional counselors we can struggle with how to fully orient our clients to the notion of the human brain as a triune or three-fold brain. Learning this structure can help you to more clearly understand why just talking is likely not enough to help you heal. While there are many instructional videos online, including many from Dan Siegel on *The Hand Model* of the brain, *my sense is that the best way to orient you to the brain-body connection is by having you color it.*

- Approach this practice as you may have approached the coloring page in Process Four on mindfulness. There is no need to fret over coloring perfectly within the lines or turning this into a work of art. Use the practice to connect to the present moment.
- You can decide to color first and then read or read as you color. The information that appears on the coloring page about the brain will hopefully give you more of an orientation about how your brain works in relationship to your body and your healing process, moving forward.

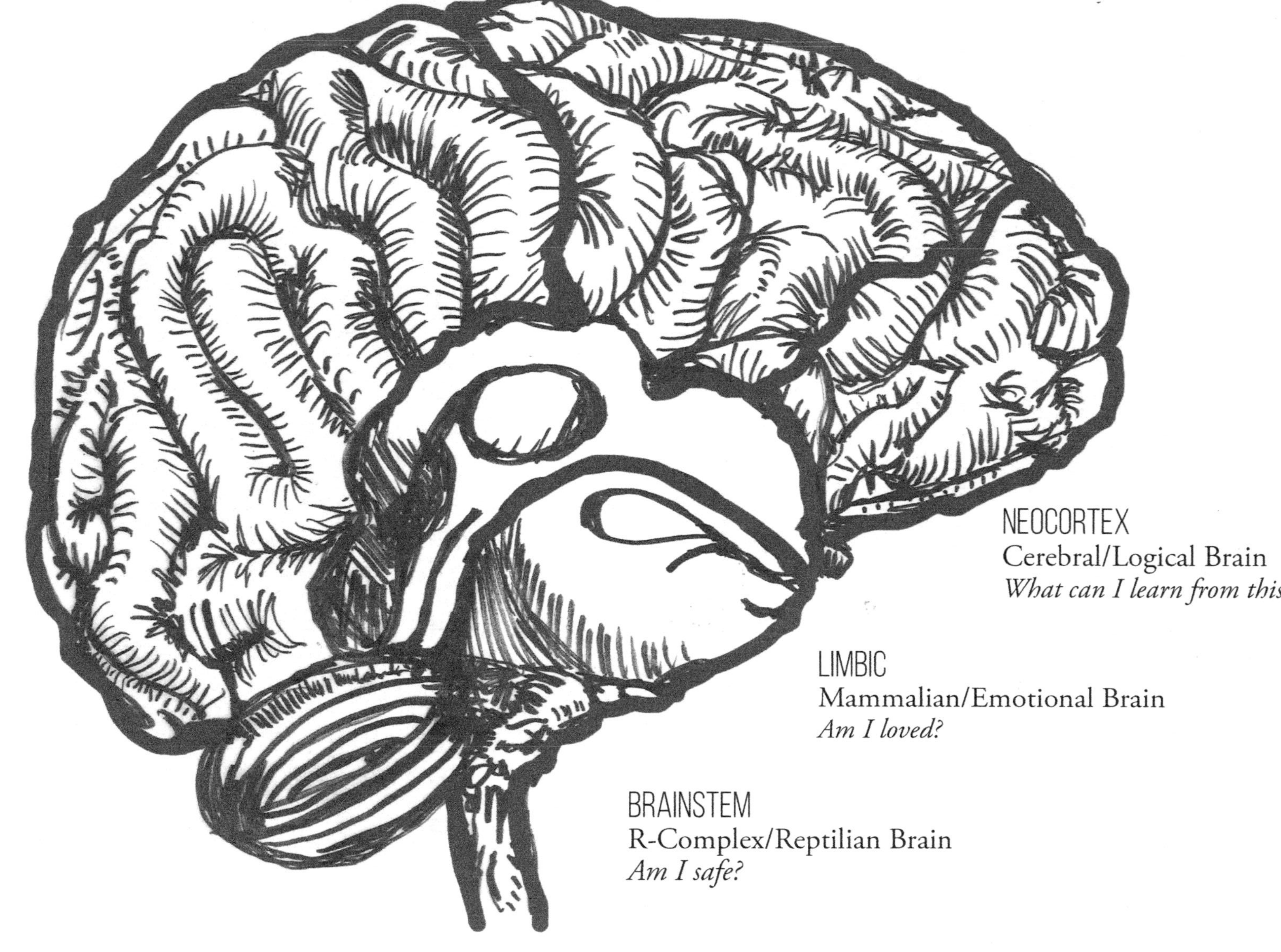
NEOCORTEX
Cerebral/Logical Brain
What can I learn from this?
LIMBIC
Mammalian/Emotional Brain
Am I loved?
BRAINSTEM
R-Complex/Reptilian Brain
Am I safe?

PRACTICE TWO

BODY SCAN IN LIVING COLOR

The Body Scan is a practice used in both yoga and many schools of Buddhist meditation. In this practice, teachers can take a short period of time, a long period, or somewhere in between to help you scan through the different parts of the body. As the teacher, leader, or clinician says the name of a body part (e.g., top of the head), you bring your attention to that area. There is a recording of me leading a traditional body scan you can access if you feel that will help you to start (see *Modification Notes* below). In this practice, we will engage in the general premise of body scan with our hands and our feet using an expressive arts twist.

- Get out two full pieces of paper (enough to trace each of your hands and each of your feet) and a pencil.
- With breath and mindful intention, trace your hands and your feet. You can trace a single hand on each page or have both hands together on the same page; the same applies to the feet.
- After you've traced these parts of your body, look at your tracing, without judgment or analysis. It's common to have judgments or analyses like, "Wow my feet are small," or "My hands are so awkward and big." If those thoughts do come up, you can use them in the next point of the exercise.

- Draw your attention to your actual hands, looking at them if possible. First your left, then your right. What do you notice in your hands? Are the sensations pleasant, unpleasant, or neutral? If these sensations had a color or colors, what would those be?
- Using your supplies for artmaking, return to the page where you traced your hands, and bring color to what you just noticed about your hands. Take as much time as you need for the practice. You may, of course, use one color or many colors to describe your experience.
- Take a breath and pause to reset, then repeat the same process with your feet.

MODIFICATION NOTES:

✓ You can view and listen to me leading a traditional body scan at: **www.traumamadesimple.com/pnp**

✓ Many people feel self-conscious about doing anything with bare feet. Although you are encouraged to use this practice as an opportunity to practice non-judgment of your body, if it feels too much for you right now, you can complete the tracing wearing socks or shoes.

✓ If disability or injury inhibits you from doing your own tracing, you can enroll a trusted friend or member of your support system to help you.

✓ Some treatment programs will lead people through a whole-body tracing for a variety of therapeutic reasons. If you have access to large butcher paper or other wrapping paper, you are welcome to do a whole-body trace (this may require assistance). After establishing the trace, you may continue this exercise in the same flow, coloring different parts and regions of your body to reflect your body scan. Doing the whole body can get intense, which is why it's indicated here only as an option for you to engage in at your own discretion.

PRACTICE THREE

CHOOSE YOUR EXPERIENCE (GUIDED MOVEMENT EXERCISE)

This practice invites you into a direct experience with moving your body. The practice itself is about working with variations in body movement that you can tailor to where you are at today. Additional options are offered in the *Modification Notes* at the end of the practice. For this Process, it's best to engage in Practices 3-5 together, so be sure to allot yourself sufficient time (about 20-25 minutes).

VARIATION 1

- Stand with your feet hip-width apart with arms at your sides. Keep your eyes open and look straight ahead. Make sure that the shoulders are as relaxed as possible; avoid letting them creep up to the ears.
- Begin on your right side: Extend the right arm out to the right side, shoulder height. Look at your hand if possible.
- Bring the hand and arm in front of you, maintaining shoulder height. Keep looking straight ahead and keep the hips squared, facing front. You can continue to stretch your arm past the midline of the body; although don't turn the body to get a bigger stretch. Keep looking straight ahead.
- Move your hand and arm along a diagonal across the body, back down to your side.

- Repeat this same process on the left side: Extend the left arm out to the left side, shoulder height. Look at your hand if possible.
- Bring the hand and arm in front of you, maintaining shoulder height. Keep looking straight ahead and keep the hips squared, facing front. You can continue to stretch your arm past the midline of the body; although don't turn the body to get a bigger stretch. Keep looking straight ahead.
- Move your hand and arm along a diagonal across the body, back down to your side.
- Continue this process at least two more times on each side, making sure to breathe as you move.
- After your final set, take a moment to come into stillness and breathe. Notice the impact of the movement on your body.

VARIATION 2

- This variation involves the same set up and engagement as the standard movements described in Variation 1. Now you are invited to deepen the intensity of the stretch.
- Begin on your right side: Extend the right arm out to the right side, shoulder height. Look at your hand if possible.
- Bring the hand and arm in front of you, maintaining shoulder height. Keep looking straight ahead and keep the hips squared, facing front. You can continue to stretch your arm past the midline of the body; although don't turn the body to get a bigger stretch. Keep looking straight ahead.
- To deepen the intensity of the stretch, use your left arm and bring it to the top of your right arm to create some resistance. Feel a deeper stretch in your whole right shoulder and arm if option for this variation.

- To disengage, lower your hand and arm along a diagonal across the body, back down to your side.
- Repeat this process on the other side.
- Continue this process at least two more times on each side, making sure to breathe as you move.
- After your final set, take a moment to come into stillness and breathe. Notice the impact of the movement on your body.

VARIATION 3

- For the final variation, instead of creating resistance to deepen your stretch, you are now invited to play with the flow a little bit more, turning this same basic movement pattern into a dance.
- Continue with the same movement pattern described in Variation 1, only this time, allow more bend in your knees, and flow in your arms. If you want to think of it as a dance, feel free. Be sure to use your breath to help you discover bigger movements.
- Continue this process at least two more times on each side, making sure to breathe as you move.
- After your final set, take a moment to come into stillness and breathe. Notice the impact of the movement on your body.

FINAL INVITATION

- Which variation seemed to have the most resonance in your body?
- Once you've noticed your body's answer to this question, take another 2–3 minutes to come into the movement variation of your choosing.
- You may elect to use music if you wish, regardless of the variation you selected.

MODIFICATION NOTES:

- ✓ This entire practice can be done sitting or lying down if you need to adapt it.
- ✓ If one arm is injured, engage in the practice on your uninjured arm and notice what you notice.
- ✓ If injury or illness inhibits use of both arms, you are always welcome to lessen the intensity of the stretches and movements described. Listen to your body and notice what feels good for you. If movement of any kind is out of the question, you are free to visualize yourself engaging in the movements.
- ✓ If you need extra guidance, be sure to visit the supplementary video where I teach this exercise at: **www.traumamadesimple.com/pnp**

PRACTICE FOUR

NOODLING-THE ART OF "GOING WITH"FREE MOVEMENT

One of my former students, dancer and performer Cornelius Hubbard, Jr., teaches a dance exercise he calls *Noodling.* Developed while he was studying dance in college, Cornelius would invoke the spirit of a noodle cooking in water—asking the body to admire the way a noodle slithers freely and easily, without stress. These are qualities that can teach us a great deal about going with the flow of life. Think of how fun and potentially beneficial it could be to take on the role of a noodle. Here are the steps to do just that in this fun, Cornelius-inspired movement practice:

- Stand up, keeping your feet as close together as possible.
- With your next breath, imagine your body beginning to be softened by gentle, bubbling water. Suspend reality for a moment and consider that this particular bubbling water would not burn you, just soften you.
- Think of taking on the role of a noodle—begin to loosen up and experience the free movement that can come about when you allow this loosening to take place. Begin with your shoulders and then let the 'noodling' move through the rest of your body.
- Continue noodling, in a mindful way. If you notice judgment or self-criticism arising, those experiences are completely normal. On your

next exhale, allow the judgment or criticism to release into the imaginal water.

- Give yourself at least 3 minutes to experiment with this, setting a timer if needed. After you move, allow yourself to be still for a few moments longer. Notice the stillness following the movement. Observe the energy in your body. If you are not doing another set of the practice, go on to Practice 5 as soon as possible.

MODIFICATION NOTES:

- ✓ Sound and music can add another dimension of fun and grounding to the exercise. If you use a music streaming service or go on YouTube, search for "bubbling water" as a sound effect. That may be all you need to get into the spirit!
- ✓ Literally any genre or series of music genres can be used for this exercise although I do recommend something light, effervescent, and bouncy to begin.
- ✓ This exercise can be fun with props like scarves or ribbons.
- ✓ You may do this exercise sitting or lying down if you cannot sustain the time on your feet.
- ✓ If you need extra guidance, be sure to visit the supplementary video where I teach this exercise at: **www.traumamadesimple.com/pnp**

PRACTICE FIVE

FEELING TONE IN LIVING COLOR

Notice the sensations present in your body after engaging in the previous two movement practices. The guiding questions and directives of this practice are based on the sensations you are noticing following Practices 3 & 4:

- You may engage in this practice standing up, sitting down, or lying down. Eyes can be closed or remain open.
- As you breathe, notice the sensations present in your body.
- Would you describe those sensations as *pleasant, unpleasant,* or *neutral*?
- It is perfectly fine to observe and notice a combination of these. For example, you may describe your stomach as neutral and your legs as unpleasant. Your shoulders may be experiencing a pleasant sensation while the rest of your body feels unpleasant.
- Take another moment to be with whatever you are experiencing, using your breath to support the process.
- Now get out a piece of paper or your journal, and whatever art materials you have available to you. If you observed pleasant sensations, how would you represent those with colors, images, and other expressions? If you observed unpleasant sensations, how would you represent those with colors, images, and other expressions? If you observed neutral sensations, how would you represent those?

- Drawing these sensations within an outline of a body is not required—it's more important that you express how you experience them. You may, however, draw an outline of the body and draw these experiences within that outline.

MODIFICATION NOTES:

- ✓ If you tried one round of Practices 3–5 standing up, you may want to try the same sequence sitting down or lying down. Observe and describe any shifts in your experience.
- ✓ If the words, *pleasant, unpleasant,* and *neutral* don't work for you, you are encouraged to use other options (e.g., healthy, unhealthy, no charge; adaptive, maladaptive, clear). Words like "good, bad, nothing" could be used with younger folks if nothing else is clicking, although try to avoid using these words if possible because they are inherently more judgmental.

FEELING TONE IN LIVING COLOR EXAMPLES

~ PEYTON MARNIE **CRAM**

~ DR. JAMIE (PRAGYA) **MARICH**

PRACTICE SIX

A LOVE LETTER TO YOUR FAVORITE BODY PART

This practice appears last in the process because it is usually the most challenging. You may be surprised by what you learned about your body and your relationship to it in the previous practices. Now you are invited to celebrate one of the pleasant, healthy, or neutral experiences that you discovered. I include neutral in that list because even being able to notice neutral (or without emotional charge) can be a big step forward in your healing progress, especially if you've been cut off from body sensations or have noticed only the unpleasant until now.

- Get out paper or journal, and something for writing.
- Begin with free writing, noting some of the insights that came up for you about your body in general during the previous practices of this process.
- As you read back your free writing, notice if there is one body part specifically that surprised you the most. Some people will say, "Wow, I didn't realize my arms were that strong," or "My feet have really carried me through a lot."
- Although you are free to reflect on some of the body parts that may still be areas of struggle, try to find one part of your body that you can truly

celebrate. This may feel like a challenge, especially if you are working with years of body hatred. People have done this exercise before focusing on some part of the body that may seem inconsequential, like how "strong and clean my fingernails are." Start somewhere—that's what's important.

- You are free to write a love letter to your whole body. If that seems impossible at this time, start with one body part. Some samples are included here if you need inspiration, although try not to let the work of others cloud your experience too much. This is your body and your words!

MODIFICATION NOTES:

✓ If a "love letter" feels too dramatic or not accessible to you today, consider writing a thank you note to your favorite or most noticeable part of the body.

✓ Like in other practices so far, the letter or note does not have to be long. 1-2 lines may be all you need.

✓ **BONUS PRACTICE:** If you are so inclined, use your camera phone or other camera to take a picture/receive an image of the body part about which you just wrote and pair it with your letter or written expression. You also have the option of using another art medium to draw.

BODY PART LOVE LETTER EXAMPLE

Photograph by LAUREN **BERGAMO**

A Love Letter to My Hips

My strength
the flow of my creativity
the power of sensuality
the channel of divine Grace
Thank you, my sweet hips
For expelling the demons
from my sacred body

Even when
I felt pain from your struggle
I know with a scared certainty
You have never once abandoned me
And as I access your precious energy
Your dances will lead me home
Steadfast, to the authentic joy that I am.

~ DR. JAMIE (PRAGYA) **MARICH**

REFLECTION QUESTIONS FOLLOWING EMBODIMENT

- Describe your personal experience with the process.
- What did you discover in your process?
- What did you learn about yourself in the process?
- What did you notice about judgment or self-criticism during the process?
- What role did the multi-modality of the art forms play in discovering what you discovered in your process?
- Which of the skills explored in this process can be applied to your overall trauma recovery or wellness plan?

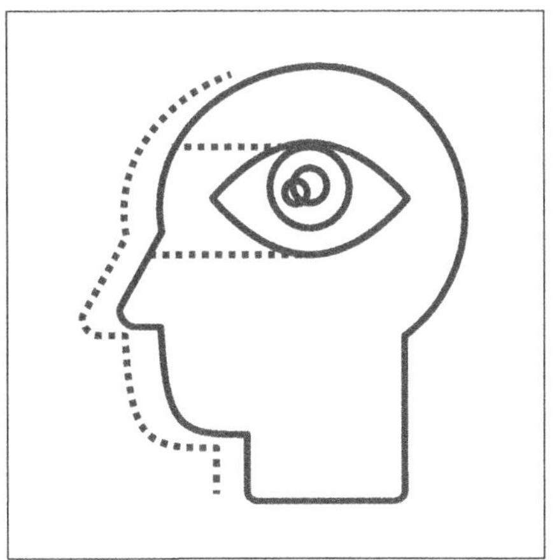

Process seven

EXPLORING THE EDGE

The concept of "the edge" (which I described earlier) is used frequently in holistic healing classes, specifically yoga and conscious dance. I commonly hear teachers and facilitators, sometimes in my own *Dancing Mindfulness* community say things like, "When you reach your edge, back off," or "Avoid pushing yourself beyond your edge." When I train new facilitators, I commonly say to them what I might hear a new client say, "What does that even mean?" or "What is an edge anyway?"

I find that the edge is a term many of us in holistic cultures have taken to using because we hear it so frequently, yet we may have never stopped to consider what it actually means. One of the goals of this process is to help us explore what "the edge" means for us in our healing journey. Another concern I have is that we've taken to equating "edge" with "boundary," and when we reach the edge, the automatic tendency, especially for our safety, is to back off. In my experience, however, growth comes when we can venture past our comfort zones, and a major step in this process is learning to make friends with our edges and see what they can teach us about forward movement.

Working with your edge is not a black and white matter. This process will challenge you to adopt quite a bit of *both/and* thinking. Yes, much of working with the edge is learning to respect the personal boundaries we've set for ourselves and listen to our body's signals about when we are not safe, or when enough may be enough for the time being. There are certain days of practice where we definitely need to honor the edge and either stay there or know that it is time to turn back to a safer haven. The other part of this reality is that optimal growth happens when we can learn to embrace our edge and not judge the experiences we are having there. Through such practices, we usually discover that we are next able to move past our comfort zones.

The system of yoga in which I primarily study and now teach, Amrit Yoga (flowing from the lineage of Swami Kripalu), works with the *edge* a great deal as a healing principle. Every time we step onto a yoga mat or into any expressive practice, we are given opportunities to explore our edges—physical, emotional, and spiritual—and work with our responses. Yogi Amrit Desai teaches, "The boundary represents an opportunity for us to encounter life with consciousness or resistance."[6] In this process, I invite you to use the expressive arts practices in a similar way. When you reach your edges, can you notice without judgment? Can you describe what you are experiencing instead of trying to label it?

---

[6] Desai, A. (2010). *The Amrit Method of Yoga Teacher Training Manual: Level 1*. Salt Springs, FL: Amrit Yoga Institute.

I encourage you to take these questions into your process as suggestions, especially when you notice discomfort. Remember that, if at any time your edge is signaling danger, you have the right to step back into any of the centering processes from the first section of the book. If you need to take this option of retreat into one of those earlier processes, my hope is that you can draw grounding and rest you need there, and then challenge yourself at some point to journey back toward, and hopefully beyond, the edge.

PRACTICE ONE

WORD CHAIN

The word chain is a practice I developed through my own experiences as a writer. When I am stuck in finding just the right word to use in a certain paragraph or poem, I start with a word that's not quite right and let myself keep free writing in a list until a word that resonates more fully emerges. I've taken to using this method much more than going to the thesaurus in recent years. From this simple brainstorming activity, I developed the word chain practice. The practice will directly link to the next one, so set adequate time aside to do both (about 10–15 minutes combined).

- Start with a word, in this case EDGE or THE EDGE.
- Set the timer for 5 minutes and just keep writing until you hear the time expire.
- Challenge yourself to keep your hand moving with words unless you are in physical pain.
- It's okay to duplicate words and for the words that come out to seem nonsensical.
- If you know another language, it's also okay for you to mix languages in your word chain.

- The intention here is to embrace the process of *going with* something, rather than analyzing or scrutinizing. No outcome is required as far as how many words you output during the 5-minute period.
- When the time is complete, take a moment to simply notice what flowed from your writing. If you wish to highlight or circle any particular resonance points you may.

MODIFICATION NOTES:

✓ If 5 minutes seems too long, especially if you have carpal tunnel or other physical issues, modify the time to 1-3 minutes.

✓ While you can type a word chain if you need to, I find the experience to be much more organic if you allow yourself to write.

✓ Choose whatever color ink, pen, or pencil you would like for the practice.

✓ See the attached image for an example of this practice.

WORD CHAIN EXAMPLE

7-9-18 – Morning Process
Word Chain

edge	love	mysterious
edgy	green	dangerous
the edge	yellow	glorious
time	joy	powerful
space	[illegible]	wonderful
boundaries	radiant	grateful
clearing	love	joyful
present	peace	soulful
presence	cat	bodyfulness
lovely	dog	mindful
sky	mouse	satiate
earth	run	
wind	leap	
one	bound	
oneness	spring	
wholeness	dance	
gratitude	radiate	
explore	luminate	
traverse	happiness	
wander	[illegible]	
joy	[illegible]	
completion	new	
grace	renew	
stirring	pregnant	
beauty	amazing	
wonder	full	
wander	growing	
last	mystery	

~ DR. JAMIE (PRAGYA) **MARICH**

PRACTICE TWO

HAIKU (OR OTHER SHORT FORM POETRY)

Now that you have a collection of words derived from the word chain practice, you are invited to create a haiku, or another short poetry form, using what you just expressed. In Japanese tradition, the haiku is a short poem of three lines designed to capture a moment. The shortness of the form, typically five syllables in the first line, seven syllables in the second line, and five syllables in the third line, can help keep things simple. In writing haiku, I am inspired by the dew drop that may appear on a blade of grass or a flower; one small capsule that feels like it contains the whole world. In linking word chain with haiku, look at the first word (edge/the edge) and the final word that you wrote down when the timer expired.

- Even if they do not seem related, challenge yourself to work with those two words together in your haiku, whether it's in the first line or other lines.
- Use some of the other words that emerged in your word chain for inspiration in composing the rest of the haiku.
- If you need an extra directive, think about how you can use this haiku to help you shape a definition of your edge.

MODIFICATION NOTE:

- ✓ While sticking to the precise 5-7-5 syllable structure of traditional haiku is not required for this practice, I do encourage you to limit the number of words you use in order to keep the words from overpowering your experience.

HAIKU EXAMPLES

Yoga Mix Haiku

In my yoga class
my breath sings with the music
and my body hums

~MYRA **RUBENSTEIN**

Dance the Line

There is a fine line
Between order and chaos
Dance the line my love

~ DR. JAMIE (PRAGYA) **MARICH**

PRACTICE THREE

RECEIVING IMAGES (PHOTOGRAPHY EXPLORATION)

I learned to love photography through my practice of expressive arts therapy after years of telling myself that I do not take good pictures. My expressive arts mentor taught me to approach photography not as a practice of taking pictures or capturing shots, rather, as a practice of *receiving images.* For me, this simple change in wording makes the practice more of a meditation than an exercise in trying to take the perfect picture. In this practice we will blend a meditative walk with the practice of receiving images, using some inspiration from the feeling tone idea of pleasant/unpleasant/neutral from the previous process.

- Set aside as much time as you can to take a meditative walk; a minimum of 20 minutes is recommended. You can walk in the area near where you live or go to any place that is interesting and accessible to you.
- Being careful not to get too judgmental or analytical about what you see, use the general descriptors of *pleasant*, *unpleasant*, and *neutral* to notice as you take your walk.
- When you see a pleasant image, allow yourself to receive that image using the camera on your smartphone or a traditional camera. If you

want to make the experience even more contemplative, take a pause before you receive the image to see if it feels (inside) as though you are meant to receive it. For instance, some people even ask a flower, "May I receive your image?"

- Repeat the same practice, in no particular order, when you encounter unpleasant or neutral images.
- You can receive multiple images in each category; please do your best to get at least one in each category.

MODIFICATION NOTES:

✓ If going outside is not accessible or safe for you, consider engaging in this same practice around your house or living space.

✓ If you are compelled to receive an image of a person on your walk, it is good ethics to ask them first, especially if their face will be seen in the image. I've taken to asking people, "May I receive your image?" instead of "May I take your picture?" even in my daily life. This gives you a good chance to educate others on this new twist to photography in expressive arts!

✓ If you don't have a smartphone or the equipment with you to do this practice, you may also use old magazines or newspapers to cut out images as if you are making a collage.

RECEIVING IMAGES EXAMPLES

(Be sure to check out the online portal for full color access to better appreciate the finer points)

~ DR. STEPHEN **DANSIGER**

PRACTICE FOUR

TAKE IT TO THE PAGE (WRITING EXPLORATION PART 1)

For this next practice in the process, observe all three of your images. You are now invited to write from the perspective of each image and notice, without judgment or analysis, what emerges. Although Parts 1 & 2 can be done at different times, you are encouraged to do them together. Allow about 30 minutes for both practices.

- Begin with the unpleasant image first. Set the timer for a minimum of five minutes. Get out paper/pen or your journal and write freely from the perspective of that person, place, thing, or situation in the image.
- What message does that unpleasant image have for you today? If you need extra direction, you can use the prompt of "I am ____________________, and today I bring you this message . . . "
- Repeat this same practice for the neutral image and the pleasant image.
- Please do your best to stay with the suggested order.
- Take a moment after each writing set to breathe and reflect on the message that you received.

MODIFICATION NOTES:

- ✓ Although you are suggested to use the order of unpleasant, neutral, pleasant for this exercise, if starting with the unpleasant is keeping you from even engaging in the practice, you may switch the order.
- ✓ If five minutes feels too much for engaging with this practice, you can always modify the time to 1-3 minutes per image.

PRACTICE FIVE

TAKE IT TO THE PAGE (WRITING EXPLORATION PART 2)

In this practice you are invited to allow your images to engage in dialogue or conversation with each other. The general instructions appear here without much commentary. Be open to what the practice reveals.

- You can approach this practice by writing in prose/short story form or writing as if you are composing a scene in a play.
  Unpleasant image:
  Pleasant image:
- Set the timer for 10 minutes. Notice what happens when you allow the unpleasant image and the pleasant image to interact.
- After the timer rings, set it for another 5 minutes. This time, allow the neutral image to enter the conversation. Notice what happens.
- If you need more time to finish up the natural flow of your writing, give yourself time.

MODIFICATION NOTES:

- ✓ As with any practice in this book, you can shorten the time spent in each section if the suggested times feel like too much right now.
- ✓ **BONUS PRACTICE:** Many students and clients I've worked with in the past end up taking their dialogue writing into another form, like poetry, or even a visual journaling piece that represents insights gained in the conversation.

PRACTICE SIX

WARRIOR POSES

Two of the classic poses in Hatha Yoga that are most easily recognizable to the general public are Warrior I and Warrior II. You can look at the pictures that accompany this practice for visual guidance. I've also provided video links of where you can watch one of my teaching partners, Jessica Sowers, and I guide the pose. The purpose of engaging in these poses (as you are able) is to develop awareness of your areas of physical edge and notice how you respond when they reveal themselves.

Warrior I

- Stand in a base mountain posture (feet together or slightly apart, noticing the strong energetic connection from your feet on the floor up through the crown of the head). Take a breath. Put your hands on your hips.
- Take a large step back with the right leg; hips stay squared to the front.
- Turn your right foot out, pointing your toes at a 45-degree angle away from the body, allowing the right foot to stay in-line with the hips in a gentle lunge position. See the photographs for options.
- Keep the left knee directly on top of the left ankle in good alignment, with the left thigh approaching parallel to the floor.

- Once you are established in this base, bring the arms out to the sides, palms facing down.
- Then, turn the palms up and express the arms in whatever way works best for your body. Common variations you see are arms directly overhead with palms facing each other, or directly overhead with fingers interlaced in temple position. You also have the option to keep the arms slightly bent in what is sometimes called goddess arms, cactus arms, or goalpost arms.
- Maintain this position as long as is sustainable. When you notice that the body wants to come out of the pose or the mind starts to give you messages like, "You can't do this anymore," or "You have to get out," see if you can deepen your breath and simply *notice* before automatically listening to those messages. This is your edge.
- Although you are not advised to push or strive, see if you can give yourself at least two full breaths here, noticing how you respond, before you automatically give in to these messages.
- Another option is to back out of the pose when the edge is screaming at you, take a few breaths to reset, and then come back into the pose.
- To release the pose, bring your hands to your side or to your chest in prayer-like position and step forward with the right foot.
- Repeat the practice on the other side. Be advised that poses may feel differently on one side than they do on the other; this is normal.

Warrior II

- To begin this pose, stand with the legs as wide apart as possible. If you are using a yoga mat, consider this reference: In Warrior I you begin with the feet facing toward the front (short side) of the mat, whereas in Warrior II, your feet are out wide towards the longer end of the mat.

- Bring your arms out to the sides of your body, shoulder height.
- Turn the left foot out, pointing it to the short side of the mat. Keep the left knee directly over the left ankle for good alignment, with this front thigh approaching parallel to the mat or floor. The knee does not bend on the opposite leg. The torso is parallel to the long side of the mat.
- Avoid having the shoulders creep up towards the ears; keep them as relaxed as possible.
- Look out over the left fingertips straight ahead, while the right arm stays behind you. Once you are here, take a deep breath.
- Maintain this position as long as is sustainable. When you notice that the body wants to come out of the pose or the mind starts to give you messages like, "You can't do this anymore," or "You have to get out," see if you can deepen your breath and again *notice* before automatically listening to those messages. This is your edge.
- Although you are not advised to push or strive, see if you can give yourself at least two full breaths here, noticing how you respond, before you automatically give in to these messages.
- Another option is to back out of the pose when the edge is screaming at you, take a few breaths to reset, and then come back into the pose.
- To release the pose, straighten the left knee and turn both feet to the long side of the mat. Rest the arms if you need before repeating on the other side.
- Repeat the practice on the other side. Be advised that poses may feel differently on one side than they do on the other; this is normal.
- After you complete the pose on both sides, step the feet together and take a moment to notice the effect of the posture in your body.

MODIFICATION NOTES:

- ✓ If you have access to the Internet, you are encouraged to watch the YouTube video to receive more guidance on modifications, including how to engage in each pose from a chair if needed. Go to: **www.traumamadesimple.com/pnp**
- ✓ Although I used the language of "yoga mat" in these descriptions to give you directional reference that corresponds with the photographs, you do not ever need a yoga mat to do yoga postures.
- ✓ Use your discretion about whether you'd like to engage in each posture barefoot or with shoes on. My only caution is to avoid practicing in socks only if you are on a hardwood or slippery floor.

WARRIOR I POSE VARIATIONS

Warrior I: Temple Variation

Warrior I: Palms Facing Variation

Warrior I: Prayer Hands Variation

Warrior I: Mudra Variation

WARRIOR II POSE VARIATIONS

Warrior II

Warrior II Variation

REFLECTION QUESTIONS FOLLOWING EXPLORING THE EDGE

- Describe your personal experience with the process.

- What did you discover in your process?

- What did you learn about yourself in the process?

- What did you notice about judgment or self-criticism during the process?

- What role did the multi-modality of the art forms play in discovering what you discovered in your process?

- Which of the skills explored in this process can be applied to your overall trauma recovery or wellness plan?

Process eight

BLOCKS TO FEELING

If you can feel it, you can heal it.

I've heard some version of this line at countless yoga, meditation, and other holistic classes over the years. Indeed, the "feel it to heal it," or "let's get in touch with our feelings" message is so widespread, it's almost become a corny cliché. I agree with the fundamental premise of the message: To truly heal our wounds, we must be able to feel what we were not allowed or able to feel at the time. Clients ask me if they must relive their trauma to heal it. I answer that question with a vehement "no." However, developing the ability to access the buried or cut off emotions is essential. And this process is much easier said than done.

One of the reasons I can't stand the "rah, rah, feel it to heal it" mentality is that teachers and leaders often make it sound so easy. The reality is that being able to access emotions and fully feel them without judging ourselves is some of the hardest work that we will ever encounter in our human journey. The primary reason is that others—parents, family members, our school systems, our places of worship, and other institutions in society—teach and effectively program us with such ugly messages about feelings and our emotional world. Take a breath and read through the following list. See if you still carry, or have carried at some time in the past, any of these messages:

- I cannot show my emotions.
- It's not safe to show my emotions.
- My emotions are too much for people.
- I cannot handle my own emotions.
- Boys/men aren't allowed to show emotions (i.e., "Man up")
- Girls can cry, but not too much.
- I cannot trust my emotions.
- My emotions get me into trouble.
- People won't like me if I say what I really feel.
- Being emotional about this means I don't trust God.
- Intellect over emotions (or similar recovery slogans)

This list is far from exhaustive, and I venture to guess that at least two messages of these are causing you suffering now or have in the past. If you've been giving yourself grief that you have not been able to clear or let go of a certain traumatic experience or block in your life and you identify with one or more of these beliefs, you may have just figured out part of the puzzle. I could fill a book with case studies of clients who have come in to see me for

EMDR or another form of trauma-focused therapy prepared to work on a major traumatic incident or other presenting issue. When I notice them shut down, block, or express trepidation about working on something that they were initially eager to address, it's typically because one of these core beliefs is standing in the way. To engage in the deeper healing process, you must identify the root of your problematic beliefs about emotions and address those first—in the context of a comprehensive treatment or wellness plan like I am laying out in this book.

Now that you have some foundational work in the skills of mindfulness, grounding, distress tolerance, and embodiment, I am going to lead you into what I believe to be the most challenging process we've visited thus far. We begin by identifying some of your stuck areas around feelings and emotions. I will lead you through other practices to help you confront and hopefully transform the beliefs that are keeping you stuck. Like with every process we've done thus far, you have the right to take a pause or retreat at any time, particularly with one of the practices you learned in the opening section of *Process Not Perfection*. If your tendency is to avoid or shut down when confronted with heavy emotion, acknowledge that tendency before you begin this process and consider making a commitment to yourself about how you will address that experience if it comes up.

PRACTICE ONE

FREE WRITING

In the opening to this chapter, I listed several of the usual suspects related to blocking beliefs surrounding emotion that affect clients and students. Every week in my clinical practice, I observe clients figuring out the exact wording that best describes the beliefs they've acquired around feeling their feelings and having emotions. This practice is a two-part exercise that will help you to identify some of your own beliefs, and begin to work with your intentions for transforming belief systems. In this process, it's ideal to engage in practices 1-3 together, allowing 15-20 minutes.

- Get out some paper or your journal and something for writing. Try to stick with black or blue ink as some work with color is introduced in a later practice.
- Set the timer for 5 minutes. Write freely on some of your beliefs—positive, negative, or neutral—about having emotions or feeling feelings. If you've done quite a bit of your own therapeutic and healing work before, you may have more positive beliefs about feelings (e.g., "I am a human being with a wide range of beautiful emotions," "I can share my feelings with safe people). If you are new to the healing process, you may have more negative beliefs around feelings (e.g., "My emotions are too much for other people to handle," "Only weak people

show emotions"). An example of a neutral statement around emotions could be, "I have feelings and that is normal." You may go longer than 5 minutes, although I challenge you to write for at least that long.

- When your free writing feels complete take a few moments to read back over it noticing while not over-analyzing. What seems to be happening in your body as you observe what ended up on the page?

MODIFICATION NOTES:

✓ You may do this exercise hand-written or typed. If you are typing, be sure that you can print it out for the next practice in the process.

✓ If 5 minutes seems too overwhelming for now, you can shorten the practice to 2-3 minutes.

PRACTICE TWO

EXPLORING COLOR

Color can be incredibly powerful. For many of us, color possesses unique, healing qualities, and can help us to better identify and explore certain experiences. Although you may have a favorite color or certain associations with colors as you enter this practice, you are encouraged to embrace it with as much of a beginner's mind as possible. When you gather your colored pencils, crayons, or markers for this practice, act as if you are an explorer in a foreign land, seeing those colors for the first time.

- Get out the free writing list from the previous practice.
- As you read each belief you wrote down, what color in your collection seems to best correspond with that belief? Without overthinking it, underline the belief with that color.
- You may also consider underlining a sentence in one color and circling a key word or words in another color(s).
- When your color-coding feels complete, take a few moments to read back over your free writing, noticing while not over-analyzing. What seems to be happening in your body as you observe what colors connected up with specific beliefs and words?

MODIFICATION NOTE:

- ✓ If you have visual problems and are not able to distinguish colors, consider drawing in symbols or images that correspond with each statement instead of using colors. You also have the option of modifying the nature of the underlines you use (e.g., using zig-zagging, dotted, straight, or bold lines). The point of the practice is to bring visual representation to your beliefs about feelings, and this modification is a way to do that without color.

PRACTICE THREE

POETRY WRITING IN LIVING COLOR

Many awesome poems begin as an experience in raw free writing. For this next practice, the challenge is to use and possibly transform some of your experiences into a living poem. Remember, what distinguishes poetry from prose is that, in poetry you determine where the lines end. In prose, the natural ending of the line on the paper or on your computer determines when you will go on to the next line. Thus, a series of belief statements can provide a nice, simple structure to write a poem. You are encouraged to write in color, using what you discovered in the previous practice, as much as possible.

- Begin your poem by writing out any positive beliefs or statements about feelings and emotions that came up in the first practice. These will serve as your first lines.
- Next, go to your neutral lines. You have the choice of leaving them as they are when placing them into your poem, or you can set an intention to develop more positive, adaptive wording about the neutral statement and use that more positive wording in your poem. To use an example from Practice 1, you may use the neutral, "I have feelings and this is normal" or set your intention to transform it into something more positive such as, "I have feelings and this is awesome!"

- Finally, go to the lines that represent the most negative messages, such as "Only weak people show emotions." What would you like to believe instead? Even if it doesn't feel true at the moment, write it down in the color of your choosing to represent the intention that you are putting out there. An example of a transformed belief could be something like, "People with big hearts show emotion."
- This is your poem! You can put a title on it if you wish. Notice whatever you notice as you read it back to yourself, or out loud.

MODIFICATION NOTES

✓ **BONUS PRACTICE:** Decorate your page with drawings, symbols, collage pieces, or other visual materials to create a frame around your poem.

✓ **BONUS PRACTICE:** Record your poem and listen to yourself read it back. What do you notice as you hear your words and intentions, presented in your own voice?

POETRY IN LIVING COLOR EXAMPLES

Disarming Dragons

Autumn drops leaves
Like jeweled dragon scales,
Shedding defenses in numbers.
Limbs exposed,
Giants rise up
And greet the dawn
In stark naked contrast.
What defenses are you holding?
What ghosts grip you still?
These shields you refuse to release -
Do they hold you in shadow
Long after your need for protection has passed?

~ MEG **HARBIN**

~ KAMALA **TAHYI**

PRACTICE FOUR

MINDFUL LISTENING

In addition to color, sound can also be used to help us identify and get in touch with our emotions. A quote commonly attributed to Leo Tolstoy declares that *music is the shorthand of emotion*. You may already have some experience with using music to connect emotionally in the spirit of this quote. In this practice and the next, we will engage in mindful listening to both instrumental tones and, if you are able, full sounds to help you more deeply sense into your emotional world.

- For part one of the practice, commit to listening to 5 instrumental pieces that primarily incorporate different instruments or sounds. You can use a music streaming service or YouTube for easiest access to a wide array of music, although traditional CDs from your own collection or a library can also be used.
- When you search, you can enter an instrument (e.g., piano music, didgeridoo) or a sound tone (e.g., bubbles, spoons clanging). Try to stay away from music with lyrics for this practice. You will have a chance to work with lyrics in the next one.
- Choose pieces that give you at least 3-4 minutes of music or sound and commit to listening all the way through.

- As you listen, notice what you are experiencing in your body. Notice what impact, if any, the piece is having on you emotionally. Keep breathing and stay in a place of non-judgment.
- When the piece is finished, spend at least a minute breathing and noticing the silence after the sound. What is the experience you are sensing in your body? Are there any colors or sensations that you seem to be aware of? What about feeling words?
- Keep your journal handy to jot down any insights that you may notice as relevant.

MODIFICATION NOTES:

✓ If 5 pieces feels like too many, try to do at least 2-3 different pieces and sound tones.

✓ You may also elect to listen to more than 5 pieces if you are getting into this practice and noticing the experiences.

✓ If access to music is not readily available to you, consider going outside and engaging in mindful listening with what you hear around you. For instance, as I write on my deck, on any given day I can hear birds, wind rustling through the trees, the humming of the air conditioner, or the roar of a lawn mower nearby. All of these sounds can elicit their own emotional and somatic experiences in my body.

PRACTICE FIVE

MAKING A PLAYLIST

This practice works with many of the same mindful listening qualities with which we worked in Practice 4. Now, you are invited to use lyrics to more fully explore your connection between music and emotion. Another one of my favorite quotes about the connection between music and feelings comes from legendary author Oscar Wilde: "Music is the art which is most nigh to tears and memory."[7]

Consider using this wisdom as inspiration while you engage in this practice. In this practice, you are invited to make a playlist of at least 3 songs to describe the evolution in process surrounding your emotional world. The playlist can be longer, although challenge yourself to find at least three songs to describe your experience.

- Choose a music streaming service where you can make a playlist. If these aren't available to you, keep in mind that you can make playlists using YouTube with the scores of musical choices available to you there.
- Begin by choosing some songs (with lyrics or instrumentals, perhaps informed by your work in Practice 4) that describe the blocks and negative beliefs around feelings and emotions identified throughout this process. Even if you are feeling relatively free of blocks right now,

[7] Wilde, O. (Commonly attributed as Epigram 88)

scan back through your history and find at least 1-2 songs that describe where you may have been at an earlier time.

- Proceed to choosing some songs that better align with your positive statements and beliefs that you identified around emotions and feelings, using what you wrote in your poetry (Practice 3) for assistance.
- Choose 1-3 songs that you can put in the middle of the songs representing the blocks/negative experiences and the songs representing the intentions/positive experiences. What instrument or song might represent a transformative quality for you? Try to work that vibe into this middle section of the playlist.

MODIFICATION NOTE:

✓ You can engage in this practice with traditional CDs if you do not have access to music streaming. If going this route, at least try to write down on a list the order of the songs as you selected them, especially if burning a compilation CD is not available to you.

PRACTICE SIX

DANCING MINDFULNESS

In the *Dancing Mindfulness*[8] community, the primary reason that we make playlists is to eventually dance to them. For this practice, you are invited to dance or move mindfully to the playlist that you constructed in Practice 5. A couple of suggestions:

- If the word dance scares you right now, approach it as mindful movement, as an extension of your meditation and expressive arts experience.
- There is no pressure to get up to your feet and perform what you may consider to be a full-scale dance. You can sit and listen to your songs and move your hands, your head, maybe tap your feet. Go to the degree that you are comfortable today while being mindful that, as I have described, the greatest growth can come from dancing with your edge.
- Pay special attention and notice if any gestures or expressions that represent your blocks come up as a pattern when you move or dance mindfully. What effect can you allow the transformative music to have on your gestures, on your body, and how you move?

[8] For more: visit the community online: www.dancingmindfulness.com or Marich, J. (2015). *Dancing Mindfulness: A Creative Path to Healing and Transformation.* Woodstock, VT: SkylightPaths Publishing.

- Observe and describe what impact listening to your music of intention or positive music may have on you being able to dance with the fullness of your emotional experiences.
- Take some time after the playlist is done to be still and quiet. Breathe and notice the impact of your movement on the stillness, going within and noticing what you are feeling and sensing in this moment. What has this movement practice taught you about your emotional world?

MODIFICATION NOTES:

✓ If dancing to the entire playlist seems like too much right now, try to dance to at least the middle three songs, using the above suggestions. Dancing to one song as a further modification is better than dancing to no songs.

✓ If you notice that the intensity of the emotion is taking you beyond your edge, remember that you can always take retreat or refuge into any of the grounding practices that you developed in the first section of this course.

✓ **BONUS PRACTICE:** Sometimes people like to take it to the page or engage in gush art after the period of suggested rest following the movement. You can use the challenge practice I offered you, "What has this movement practice taught you about your emotional world?" if you need the assistance.

REFLECTION QUESTIONS FOLLOWING BLOCKS TO FEELING

- Describe your personal experience with the process.
- What did you discover in your process?
- What did you learn about yourself in the process?
- What did you notice about judgment or self-criticism during the process?
- What role did the multi-modality of the art forms play in discovering what you discovered in your process?
- Which of the skills explored in this process can be applied to your overall trauma recovery or wellness plan?

Process Nine

LIVING OUTSIDE OF THE BOX

Unhealed trauma can make us feel boxed in—trapped into roles, life scripts, and patterns that do not serve us. In the previous process, I challenged you to identify and explore the various beliefs or messages that may keep you stuck in the arena of emotions. If you engaged in that process, I believe you are ready for this next area of inquiry and discovery. See if any of these internal belief systems may be part of your experience, either presently or at some point in the past:

- I am trapped.
- I cannot let it out.
- I cannot stand it.

- I do not belong.
- I don't fit in with this family/this town/this school.
- I must do what I'm told.
- I have to stick to the script for good behavior.
- Girls are expected to get married and raise kids.
- A real man wouldn't work in this field (and other gendered messages).
- I must behave in a certain way because my religion tells me to.
- My family knows what is best for me.

Like with the list of beliefs about feelings and emotions, this list is not exhaustive. If reading this list of beliefs brought up others for you, honor what those may be and be prepared to work on them.

For this process, the metaphor and concept of the box will be used for our practices. In the first section of this book, we talked about a container as being a positive resource we can develop to hold issues that we are not quite ready to handle. However, sometimes we can contain such difficulties for too long; without working on them we can become "boxed in" and affected by a whole host of negative symptoms. Additionally, all the beliefs highlighted so far represent ways that people, society, and the messages we've received as the result of our adverse life experiences, can keep us stuck. This can keep us from living our fullest lives and reaching the intentions we have set for our own health and wellness.

In casual English, we often pay tribute to creative thinkers by saying that they "think outside the box." This process will help you to do that or to do it more fully. You may even reach the point where you can throw out the box all together and live life with a greater sense of freedom and authenticity. As with every other process, use the skills and practices you cultivated in the first section of the book as an anchor for grounding and safety if you need them. However, notice whether your retreat into these practices truly serves you or keeps you more boxed in.

PRACTICE ONE

FREE WRITING–METAPHOR AND MEANING

In the opening to this process, I listed several of the beliefs that relate to what it means to live within the box. If the metaphor of the box doesn't work for you, think of others that might (e.g., bird in a cage, prisoner in a dungeon, being made to stick to a rigid script that doesn't work for you). This practice is a combined exercise that will help you to identify some of your own beliefs/cognition statements and metaphors. This prepares you for working on release and transformation. Get out some paper or your journal and something for writing. You can write in standard black/blue, or use fitting colors.

- Set the timer for 5 minutes. Write freely on the belief statements and metaphors that describe your particular forms of confinement, past or present (see the opening to this practice for some examples if you are stuck). If you've done your own therapeutic and healing work before, you may have more positive beliefs, based on experience, about your ability to break free (e.g., "I am a unique soul," or "I live outside the lines"). Your beliefs may also feel more confined, whether you are new to the healing process or you've been at this for a while (e.g., "It's too risky to be myself," or "I will let people down if I am authentic"). You may go longer than 5 minutes, although I challenge you to write for at least that long.

- When your free writing feels complete, take a few moments to read back over your free writing, noticing while not over-analyzing. What seems to be happening in your body as you observe what ended up on the page?

MODIFICATION NOTES:

- ✓ You may do this exercise hand-written or typed.
- ✓ If 5 minutes seems too overwhelming for now, you can shorten the practice to 2-3 minutes.
- ✓ If words do not seem like they can fully reflect your experiences, you may replace the writing of belief statements or metaphors with drawing or collage. Although we will work visually in other practices in this process, you may already be feeling that call.

METAPHOR AND MEANING FREE WRITING EXAMPLES

Entombed

Sinking into my physical shell.
Entombing and suffocating.
Tearing at the walls placed there.
Built there.
What of escape?
From the turmoil boiling at the base of my being.
One thought.
One thought.
One thought.
Cascading into an avalanche that I cannot out run.
Sit.
Curl up.
Bow your head.
If you do not move, you will not be seen.
Inhale.
Hold.
Hold.
Hold.
"This is your shame,"
it whispers.

~ PEYTON MARNIE **CRAM**

To Love Her

(Based on a first line by Mary Oliver from "The Hummingbird")

The green wheel of her wings
Are powered by sacred breath
The life force of this and every age

Her wings take her to the corners of the earth
Where Divine Order wills her flight
She is vibrant, she is free

She soars with the wisdom of the ages
She owns her beauty and her grace while
Knowing when to rest into her vulnerability

Others have tried to clip her wings
Threatened by their span and their reach
And there was a time she almost let them win

Yet as wise friends observe...
What would be the point of loving her?
To love her is to let her fly

~ DR. JAMIE (PRAGYA) **MARICH**

PRACTICE TWO

3D VISUAL MEDITATION–PART 1

Author and popular online presence Jaeda deWalt asserts, "Don't let others box you into what they think you should be. . . . Trust that in living true to yourself you will attract people who support and love you, just as you are." In this meditative practice, you are invited to literally make a box that represents your confinement. Seeing what you now know internally or what you've just written about on paper can be a game changer. In this process, it's ideal to engage in practices 2–3 together, allowing 15–20 minutes after you've gathered the necessary materials described in this practice.

- If the metaphor of the *box* works well for you, find a box of any kind—a shoe box, a jewelry box, a large shipping box.
- If you need to use an alternative, it may be more difficult although it is doable. Craft stores are great places to find bird cages for decorating, for instance, and you may have an old play script hanging around. Even an old book that represents the messages of your confinement could work for these purposes.
- Write any messages or beliefs that you identified with your confinement in Practice 1 on the inside of the box or somewhere within your alternate representation if you are not using a box.
- Now, destroy the box or your alternative in whatever way works for you! You may choose to crush the box, burn it (please go outside and be safe

if this is your choice), or find another way to transform it. Be as creative as possible with your intention and method to transform the visual representation of your confinement.

- After you've destroyed or transformed the visual appearance of the box in whatever way works for you today, take a few minutes to breathe and to notice your experience without judgment. Even if it feels like you've "faked it" for the purposes of this practice, know that there is still tremendous power in setting intention, and you've just done that with this practice on a visual plane.
- The second part of this meditation will follow after you engage in Practices 3 and 4.

MODIFICATION NOTE:

✓ If nothing suitable approximating a box is available to you in three-dimensional form, you can use a two-dimensional image (magazine cut out, drawing, image printed from computer)

PRACTICE THREE

MOVEMENT EXPLORATION

People experience different things after the previous practice. You may be abuzz with sensations, numbed out, or somewhere in the middle. For this practice, you are invited into some gentle movement to further mine the wisdom your body may be giving you.

- In the spirit of *dancing mindfulness* described several times in this book, take a few moments to move or simply be with the sensations evident in your body right now.
- You are invited to spend 2-3 minutes moving in silence, and then if it feels organic to put some music on, you may.
- If it hasn't happened already, notice if there is a gesture or a movement that represents what it means for you to be confined or boxed in. Come into that gesture or movement and take a few moments to breathe there.
- As you are able, let the movement and your breath working together bring you out of that gesture or movement and into something different. What do you notice?

- What would a gesture or movement of freedom (or moving away from confinement) feel like in your body? Like the previous practice, even if it feels like you're "faking it," there is great power in setting intention. To intone the words of dance/movement therapist Irmgard Bartenieff, "Intention organizes the neuromuscular system."

MODIFICATION NOTES:

✓ Like with all movement practices in this book, there is no pressure to do this standing up. Some of my most powerful experiences with this practice have come when I sit or lie down.

✓ Be very gentle with yourself. Tears and other sensations or sounds of release are very normal and likely when engaging in this practice. If your sense is telling you that it feels safer to do this in the presence of a trusted friend or member of your support system, honor that.

PRACTICE FOUR

FULL PLAYLIST AND *DANCING MINDFULNESS* EXPLORATION

In many places throughout this book, I've invited you to make playlists and then further extend an invitation to move with the music on that playlist. In this practice you are invited to use what you have learned to help you further the experience of moving from your own confinement into something more authentic, meaningful, and free.

- Begin this practice by making your playlist. Remember that playlists can be as short as three songs (the suggested minimum to capture a beginning, a middle, and an end flow). The length is completely up to you.
- Begin by choosing some songs or sounds that represent being boxed in or confined.
- Allow yourself to choose at least one song that best represents the experience of breaking free. If there's not a song you can identify, think of an instrument that would best represent this quality for you and bring that into your playlist.
- Conclude with songs that represent freedom, awakening, and authenticity. Even if it feels like you're not truly there yet, remember what you have learned thus far in the process about the power of setting intentions.

- Once the playlist is complete, you can listen to it the whole way through before dancing to it, or you may elect to set aside the needed time to dance the entire playlist.
- After your *Dancing Mindfulness* practice is complete, you may elect to absorb it in silent meditation, free write in your journal, or immediately go on to the last two practices in this process.

MODIFICATION NOTES:

✓ Remember that YouTube allows you to make a playlist of songs even if you don't have access to a streaming service for music.

✓ If a full range of movement isn't available to you, remember that you can do the entire practice sitting or lying down. Some people report that visualizing themselves dancing as they would like to, even if their physical body doesn't permit it, is a viable and very healing modification.

PRACTICE FIVE

3D VISUALIZATION–PART 2

Return to the visual meditation that you created in Practice 2. What are you noticing now about the box or other symbol of your confinement that you destroyed or otherwise transformed?

This practice is very simple in instructions although it can be potentially challenging and emotional to execute.

- Is there any other way you wish to further change the appearance of your box or symbol of your confinement?
- Let your imagination and creativity run wild. Do you see any paths forward for creating a new art piece out of the rubble and remains?
- Keep an open mind, heart, and spirit about what your continuing art making process can teach you about transformation and breaking free.

MODIFICATION NOTE:

✓ As with the movement exploration in Practice 3, if it feels safer for you to engage in this practice in the presence of a friend or trusted member of your support system, honor that.

PRACTICE SIX

FAIRY TALE WRITING

The fairy tale is a time-honored story structure familiar to many cultures. While we may be used to the clichés of fairy tale like "Once upon a time," the familiarity of that structure may help us to further embrace our own story of transformation. In many beloved fairy tales and legends, captivity is a common theme and the rescue from captivity can make for some compelling drama! This practice will challenge you to at least begin the process of writing your own fairy tale or legend.

- Begin your story with "Once upon a time . . ." Even if the term "fairy tale" does not feel appropriate to you and you wish to embrace this more as a legend or epic poem, consider using the "Once upon a time" opener. It can help more fully lead you into the telling of what happened to put you into captivity.
- You can revisit Process 2 on Breathing if you need to draw some inspiration in writing the flow of your story. Recall what elements you used there to bring about transformation and consider if those would fit here as well.
- Although your story is not required to have a specific length, allow it to have a beginning, a middle, and an end.

- In 12-step programs, there's a saying that can work well for fairy tale writing too: What it was like, what happened, and what it's like now.
- Unlike conventional fairy tales, this one does **not** have to end with "happily ever after." In my experience, the best feminist rewrite of fairy tales is more likely to wrap up with, "And who can tell how any story will truly end?" At very least, you are encouraged to end your fairy tale on a note of hope, even if that hope is simply the setting of intention.

MODIFICATION NOTES:

✓ If writing this much does not feel available to you physically, you can verbally tell the story into a recording device or to a trusted friend.

✓ **BONUS PRACTICE**: Even if you are writing the story, consider recording yourself reading it and then listen back. Notice the experience. If you feel led to share your reading publicly or with a trusted member of your support system, honor that prompting.

✓ If you need an example of an "outside the box" spin on a fairy tale for inspiration, visit the online resources portal and check out Dr. Jamie's *Be A Dragon* at **www.traumamadesimple.com/pnp**

REFLECTION QUESTIONS FOLLOWING LIVING OUTSIDE THE BOX

- Describe your personal experience with the process.

- What did you discover in your process?

- What did you learn about yourself in the process?

- What did you notice about judgment or self-criticism during the process?

- What role did the multi-modality of the art forms play in discovering what you discovered in your process?

- Which of the skills explored in this process can be applied to your overall trauma recovery or wellness plan?

Process ten

EMBRACING THE STORY

I get chills every time I hear or read Muriel Rukeyser's words: "The universe is made of stories, not atoms." Too often, psychology and other helping professions attempt to turn the lived experience of human beings into hard science, putting numbers, scales, and metrics on our pain and our recovery. In my career as a helping professional, I've seen the push for numbers-based research attempt to drain the soul out of our work. Such research, which informs the construction of rigid treatment manuals and protocols, attempts to put human beings and our experiences into boxes, the very same issue described in detail as problematic in the previous process. Although I am not opposed to this type of research and inquiry outright, I fear that the helping professions have valued it over our own personalized stories of transformation and healing in deciding what works in recovery. Many years ago when I shared this sentiment in a training I led, a participant responded with the wisdom of Muriel Rukeyser, a great poet and feminist, and I've felt vindicated ever since!

Being in process with our stories is vital to the healing process. Whether we are being led to release old stories and old storylines that no longer serve us, or embrace facets of our own personal stories with new meaning, we can find great reward in doing this work. In the practice of *Dancing Mindfulness* as a therapeutic method, story is one of the seven major elements. In my book, *Dancing Mindfulness: A Creative Path to Healing and Transformation,* I define story as:

> The narrative of experience, which can be manifested and expressed in a variety of ways. Stories can be told in the first, second, or third person. Stories can be the lived experience of the mindful dancer, or a character that emerges during a given dance. Most important within the *dancing mindfulness* practice is that genuineness guides the telling of your story, and that the story be told in an atmosphere of non-judgment.

In *Process Not Perfection*, it is my great privilege to expand this definition of story to encompass all expressive arts and expressive artists.

If you have not yet visited the practice of Embrace-Release-Embrace (Practice 5 in Process 4 on Mindfulness), you are encouraged to do that before engaging in this Process of Embracing the Story. The lens through which I take you into this deeper work on story is based largely on these mindful teachings. You may choose to incorporate other descriptions like owning your story or claiming your story, as terms like these have become quite popular in the larger world of psychology and self-help. However, I've maintained throughout my career that the concept of *embrace* is the most mindful word we can apply to our stories in doing this type of work.

As I wrote in *Dancing Mindfulness*, "When I think of embracing the stories that form the collage of my own personal history, I see a picture of me giving myself a hug and accepting it all—the joy and the sorrow, the worthiness and the shame, what has been and what is yet to be. In embracing myself in this way, I embrace acceptance and self-compassion."

One of my dear friends and mentors, Dr. Paschal Baute, offers a mindful reflection on the importance of *embrace* that can set the tone for full healing and transformation appropriate to this section of the book. In his memoir, *Resilience of a Dream Catcher: A Spiritual Memoir,* he writes that "Mindfulness is openness to embrace whatever life presents, with awareness of the possibilities of the moment. It is an awakening to the full awareness. *Resilience* is the act of transcending and transforming that moment, threat, challenge or loss. Much overlap exists. *Being mindful is already an act of transcending one's circumstances.*" [9]

You are already present in the here and now! I honor you for arriving at this moment, to this time, and to this place. Take a minute to breathe and really savor it. You are already transcending your circumstances and transforming your pain. When your breath leads you, let's continue onward with the journey . . .

---

[9] Baute, P. (2014). *Resilience of a dreamcatcher: A spiritual memoir*. Lexington, KY: Baute Publishing/ Smashwords Publishing.

PRACTICE ONE

CONNECTING WITH ANOTHER'S STORY

My first favorite story was *The Wizard of Oz.* I initially watched the classic MGM telling of L. Frank Baum's tale featuring the incomparable Judy Garland when I was about 5 years-old and I simply fell in love. Through the various seasons of my life, I've connected with Dorothy Gale as a role model, a protector figure, a friend, and in recent years, as a mythical embodiment of my healing story. Your person may be completely different. Your first sense of connection with another's story may be that of a spiritual or religious/spiritual figure. In this practice, you are invited to connect with the sacred story of another and engage in dialogue with that individual.

- Choose a character whose story you have long admired. Historical figures, fictional characters, religious and spiritual figures, and people whose stories are told in songs or poems are all fair game.
- For the first part of the practice, write a letter to the person you selected. Be sure to introduce yourself, and tell them what you admire about their journey and their story. If "admire" is not the right word, explain to them why you connect with their story so much.
- For the second part of the practice, write a letter back to you from the perspective of that character. What do they have to say to you? Are there any specific messages they wish to convey?

MODIFICATION NOTES:

- ✓ If words are not flowing very easily, you always have the option to use images. Another option is to think in terms of sending your character a postcard. What image would be on the front of the post card?
- ✓ If they were to send you a post card in return, what image would be on theirs?
- ✓ If you can't settle on one character for this practice, you can engage in it with multiple characters.

CONNECTING WITH ANOTHER'S STORY EXAMPLE

Dear Cinderella,
My name is Katie and I admired you so much as a child. Your story and image still warm my heart. As I watched you work so hard to please your stepmother and sisters, I always admired your strength for not running away. You went to your own little corner, sang and danced the night away. I loved watching you laugh, love life and dream of all the things you could be. I loved your humility and kindness, always putting others before yourself. The glass slipper was so beautiful and although rather transparent, saved your life in so many ways. Your fairy godmother gave you everything just at the right time and helped you realize you had everything you needed to succeed. Congratulations for following your heart, fearlessly speaking up and being true to yourself.

~ KATIE **GIFFORD**

PRACTICE TWO

WRITING A SCENE

Now that you and your character have exchanged letters, it's time to imagine that the two of you will meet up in person!

- You are the author of this story and get to create the era, the scene of your meeting, and the conditions in which you will meet. Begin your scene by writing a short description of this setting as if you are writing the stage directions for a play.
- Now write the scene—assume that the two of you are already familiar with each other from exchanging correspondence.
- Use dialogue as if you are writing a stage play to capture the essence of your conversation. For example:

JAMIE: Dorothy, do those ruby slippers hurt?
DOROTHY: Yes, they are the most uncomfortable things ever. I took them off as soon as they got me home!

- The scene can be as long or as short as you need it to be. Give it enough time for a natural conversation to unfold and notice the impact that the conversation is having on you.
- Write a natural ending to the scene and as you do, notice if the other person's essential message for you from their initial letter has changed in any way.

MODIFICATION NOTES:

- ✓ If you couldn't settle on one character in Practice 1 and opted for several, you can write your scene for multiple characters.
- ✓ If you can't imagine talking to the character you selected or they are not a person of many words, what images would you draw for each other? Bring those to life if that feels more organic.

WRITING A SCENE EXAMPLE

Katie: What do you consider your greatest strength?
Cinderella: To embrace every day and in every way be good to myself.
Katie: How much time does it take?
Cinderella: All the time you have in the world.
Katie: How did you stay so strong with all the struggles you faced with the people who were supposed to love you unconditionally?
Cinderella: My father was always there, loving me in his own gentle way. He loved everyone.
Katie: Why didn't he protect you and make them stop?
Cinderella: I don't think he realized the pain her words caused. My step mother had him snowed and she was a great pretender. He didn't realize my sensitivity was greater than my ingrained humility. It was very important to him that no matter what happened, I stayed humble. I think he felt it was the secret to life. He possibly thought if he loved her enough, that magically the love would filter through to the rest of us.
Katie: Since your mother has passed, do you feel guilty that your siblings are no longer part of your life?
Cinderella: No, just like their mother, they don't have it in them to love others like they love themselves.

Katie: How do you cope with that?

Cinderella: No matter how hard you try to make others love you, it really is "Impossible". Some things in life are just that, "Impossible" and not even the Fairy Godmother can change their minds. Everyone has a free will to be who they want to be and love to the degree they want to love. Focus on "your world" and what means most to you and nothing will be "Impossible".

Katie: Things have often felt impossible.

Cinderella: Now look closely in this crystal ball, see there you have been nurtured by everyone along your journey. They were all fairies. Now, not necessarily the ones you would expect. At times, you didn't even see them for who they really were because you couldn't see their wings. They were all fairy gatekeepers, keeping watch over you and helping you find everything you needed for the journey.

Katie: I want to be free from feeling like things are out of reach and impossible.

Cinderella: You hold the key and the power is deep inside you.

Katie: So, what is the key to living happily ever after?

Cinderella: It is what you have given to others your entire life, Love.

Katie: "What's love got to do with it? But, I thought love was just a second-hand emotion."

Cinderella: Everything! Now, it is your turn to love yourself unconditionally.

Katie: I'm just afraid I will never be good enough.

Cinderella: You have always given your best and believe me, that is more than good enough! Oh yes, I have a gift for you! It is from one of your fairy Godmothers.

Katie: Naomi?

Cinderella: Yes, here they are–now try them on! They were her favorite pair and she said she wouldn't be needing them anymore. She wanted you to have them.

Katie: Blue glass slippers! They fit!

Cinderella: They look stunning! Oh my, it is getting late. So you must get going, there is still so much you need to do to get ready for the great celebration.

Katie: Thank you Cinderella, I will. When will I see you and Naomi again?

Cinderella: At the Grand Ball of course! It will be at 777 Aurous Ave. Naomi said she will be waiting for you just outside by the Gate of Pearls.

Katie: What time?

Cinderella: At the stroke of midnight, of course!

Katie: But how will I get there?

Cinderella: Just tell the coachman, he just took Naomi there and certainly knows the way.

Katie: Thank you! Please tell Naomi I love the slippers and they fit perfectly!

Cinderella: She just knew they would!

Katie: I can hardly wait!

Cinderella: And remember, don't be late!

~ KATIE **GIFFORD**

PRACTICE THREE

RELEASING THE STORYLINES (MOVEMENT PRACTICE)

Many Buddhist traditions caution practitioners not to remain too attached to your *storylines*, especially those that are rigidly defined or contribute to your sense of feeling stuck. This teaching may be a struggle for those new to the mindful healing process that have been told so much about *owning* or *embracing* their stories to heal. For me the answer is *both/and*. To fully embrace our stories of healing and transformation, we must first let go of those old, ugly stories about ourselves that we've told again and again.

I developed the movement practice described here in collaboration with *Dancing Mindfulness* facilitator Dr. Kirsten Koenig, a member of the Blackfeet nation and expert at adapting Native American healing practices for general clinical and wellness settings.

- Find a dedicated space for moving along the floor.
- You may choose a piece of instrumental music for the first part of this practice or move in silence.
- Take a few breaths and begin to turn inward. Ask yourself, "What are the old stories that keep me from moving forward? What words, images, or symbols go along with those stories and their ugly messages?"

- Use your feet to begin writing the words, images, or symbols on the ground. You may also elect to get down to the ground and write these words, images or symbols with your hands. Take as much time as you need, anywhere from 1-3 songs (about 5-10 minutes of music).
- Find a piece of music that references the water, or find a water sound (e.g., ocean, river, rapids, rain) on your streaming service or on YouTube.
- Imagine that the entire room in which you are dancing begins to fill with water. This is not the type of water that will hurt you or drown you, it is the water that is designed to clear away and wash out these storylines you wish to release to the flow of universal healing.
- Just go with it: If your practice is calling you to dance to the water music, respond to the call of that movement. If stillness is required to notice the musical water and its cleansing effects, honor that internal prompting.
- Take as much time in the silence as you need, noticing your body, after the water has worked its healing power.

MODIFICATION NOTES:

✓ You may use your hands to trace your words, images, or symbols on the walls in place of or in addition to the floor.

✓ If you are confined to sitting or lying down and cannot reach the floor or walls, you may also trace your words, images or symbols in the air and still invoke the same presence of water.

✓ If water is a source of trauma for you that may require professional intervention to work through, you may consider using the element of earth to help you release the words, images, or symbols. After you've traced them into the floor, imagine that a healing energy from deep in the earth begins to absorb them back into the earth where they can be fully transformed.

PRACTICE FOUR

THE SOUNDTRACK OF YOUR LIFE (PLAYLIST EXERCISE)

This book has provided several opportunities for you to work with playlists. In this practice, you are invited to compose the playlist of your life story, using your streaming services or YouTube. You can compose your playlist chronologically through the eras of your life, or along the different themes that have made your life uniquely your own. However, you can take this practice in a thousand different directions. The following guidelines also contain the modification notes for this practice:

- The playlist can be as long or as short as you need it to be. I recommend a minimum of three songs.
- Honor a beginning—middle—end structure in composing your playlist. If you gravitate toward 12-step recovery language, you can use the themes of *what it was like, what happened,* and *what it is like now* in finding your songs and composing your playlist.
- If you don't think you are a person who knows music and song titles well enough to adequately do this exercise, type in a few key theme words into your music streaming service or YouTube. See what comes up, listen, and if it resonates, add it to your playlist.

- Wherever your playlist leads you, I suggest that you allow the last song on the list to be one that seals in your intention for healing and growth going forward.
- Use a mixture of genres. Additionally, even though this exercise is in the DEEPENING section of the book, please do not be bashful about using songs that are lighthearted or humorous. I draw great inspiration from the words of comedian Hannah Gadsby in her groundbreaking standup comedy show, *Nanette*: "Laughter is not our medicine, stories hold our cure. Laughter is just the honey that sweetens the bitter medicine." So wherever your playlist may take you, I challenge you to choose at least one song that makes you laugh from your belly, out loud and unashamed!

PRACTICE FIVE

STORYDANCING

In *Dancing Mindfulness* and many other conscious dance forms, one of the simplest prompts a facilitator can give a practitioner is: "Tell your story to the dance floor." Alternate wordings can include, *release your story to the dance floor*, *share your story with the earth*, or simply *dance your story*. One of my favorites challenges, reflecting my expressive arts soul: *Allow the dance floor to be the canvas. Your body is your paintbrush. Your breath is the paint and spirit moves the paintbrush. Go with it . . .*

- Use any of the suggestions described here to inspire you for this practice. The playlist you created in Practice 4 will serve as your music for *Storydancing*.
- If dancing the whole playlist at one time feels like too much physically or emotionally, know that you can break it up over 2–3 days or take as many breaks as you need. Remember that stillness is also part of the dance.
- When you have danced the entire playlist take a few moments to be in stillness with your experience.

MODIFICATION NOTES:

- ✓ If it feels safer for you to engage in the *Storydancing* practice if it is witnessed by a trusted friend or member of your support group, honor that prompting.
- ✓ You may decide to dance the entire playlist privately and then share a song or two that particularly resonated with someone (this is optional of course).
- ✓ **BONUS PRACTICE:** If you need to take some time free writing your responses in your journal before transitioning to the final practice, please take some time to do that.

PRACTICE SIX

THE MURAL OF TRANSFORMATION

The first mural I ever saw was at the public library on the West Side of Youngstown where I grew up. It was a visual presentation of Ohio's state history. The little kid in me thought it would be super cool to paint a bunch of connecting images on a wall! While you are not expected to paint on the walls of your living space for this exercise, you are asked to channel the spirit of what a mural means and create your own, inspired by your story and what you've learned about embracing it throughout this process.

- If painting on the wall isn't feasible to you (I suspect that for most of you it is not), find something that you can use to affix to the wall temporarily. The plain white side of wrapping paper works, as does butcher paper, or a plain white/newsprint tablecloth.
- Use this long piece of paper as the background for your story. You can paint, draw, or use collage elements. Your options are limitless, bound only by the supplies you are able and willing to access. A combination of images and words may be used.
- Consider going online and typing "mural" into a search engine to see some examples if you are stuck. While you can be inspired by the images, endeavor to make the work a true expression of your uniqueness.

MODIFICATION NOTES:

- ✓ If a large enough piece of paper isn't accessible to you, you can tape together several pieces of standard size pages and make a mural in miniature right on your table space.
- ✓ If the idea of a mural feels too daunting for you, especially if you are still coming to terms with your emotional world, consider using our modern hieroglyphic system—emojis—to help you express the story of your life and transformation (see my example below).
- ✓ While a standard collage is also an option, a mural allows for more of a sequential, progressive feel to the story. Think about the beginning, middle, and end structure suggested in the Storydancing practice. Allow that to manifest on the mural.

~ MICHELLE **TOMPKINS**

~ EDWARD **CARSON, ESQ**

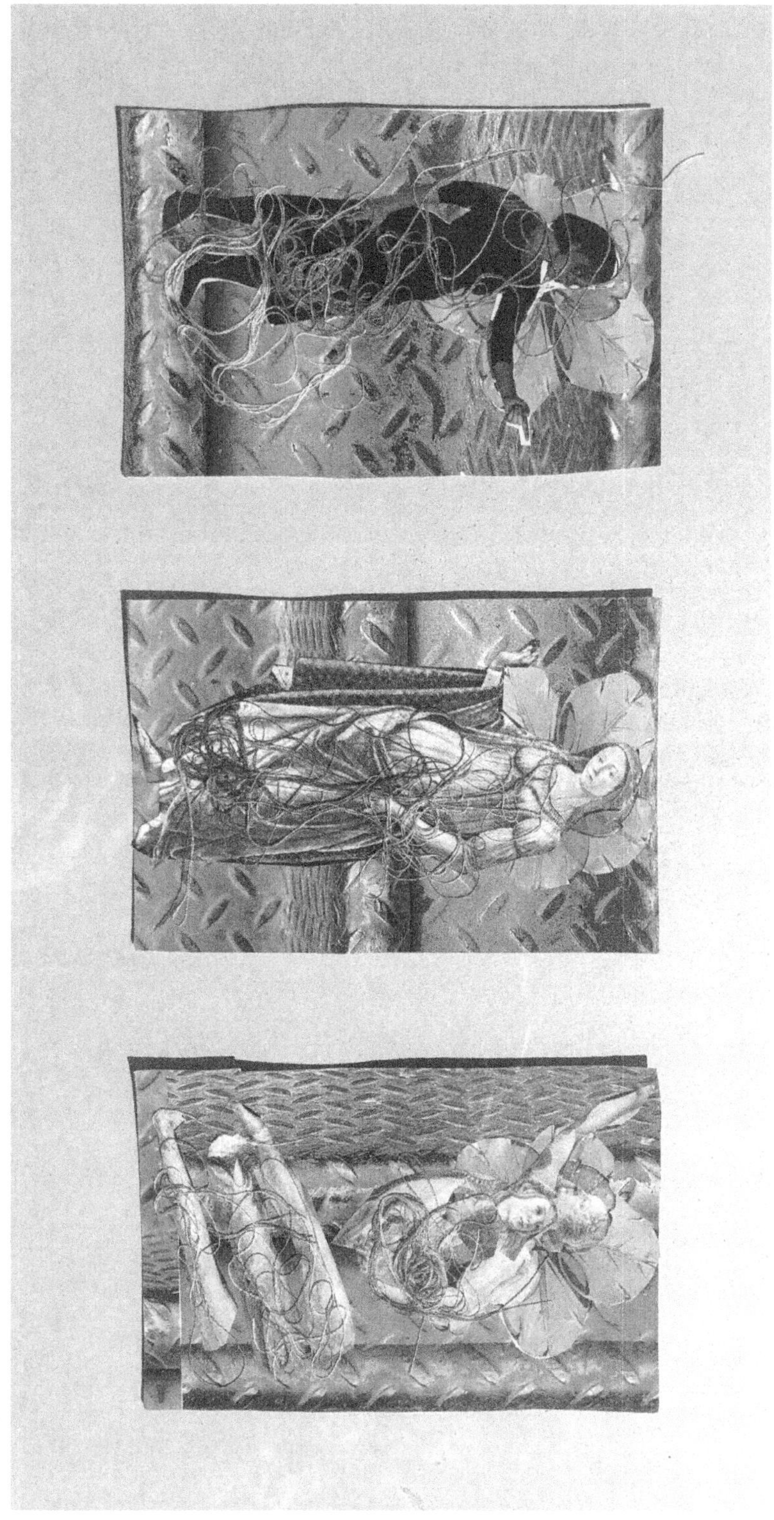

EMOJI MODIFICATION EXAMPLE

~ DR. JAMIE (PRAGYA) **MARICH**

REFLECTION QUESTIONS FOLLOWING EMBRACING THE STORY

- Describe your personal experience with the process.
- What did you discover in your process?
- What did you learn about yourself in the process?
- What did you notice about judgment or self-criticism during the process?
- What role did the multi-modality of the art forms play in discovering what you discovered in your process?
- Which of the skills explored in this process can be applied to your overall trauma recovery or wellness plan?

Section 3: MANIFESTING

Process eleven

ADAPTABILITY & FLEXIBILITY

Living in process opens up your ability to constantly see connections and opportunities for deepening your practice. Embracing life this way can allow us to better deal with the ebbs and flows of our daily existence. The purpose of any conscious practice is not to make the stress stop; our practices do not make us immune to the catastrophes, traumas, and turmoil of life. What we find is that consistent engagement in conscious practice allows us to better deal with the stress that life brings our way.

If you are in a 12-step recovery fellowship you've likely heard the phrase "life on life's terms." I used to hate that saying and was never really sure what it meant. Over the years, my practice has shown me I am in control of very little—only my own actions and responses to those stressors that are inevitable. Through the consistent practice of mindfulness, yoga, and all the expressive arts, I've managed to accept whatever the flow of life brings my way and inevitably transform my pain and suffering into works of arts.

The focus of this process is on two skills that are vital for long-term recovery and wellness: adaptability and flexibility. Being rigid and reactive is not optimal for dealing with the inevitable onslaught of life. One of my primary teachers, Yogi Amrit Desai, asserts that "life is perpetual therapeutic irritation." It's a harsh truth, yet one I've decided to accept instead of fight. From this place of acceptance, I can work on being more adaptive and flexible, especially when life doesn't seem to be going my way. The impact of trauma can leave us feeling very reactive when we are faced with stress. This can show up in the form of temper tantrums, outbursts of anger, or being excessively hypervigilant or jumpy. While these are classic symptoms of hyperarousal, sometimes the reactivity plays out on the opposite end of the spectrum where we can find ourselves shutting down, zoning out, and becoming numb to life.

Working with the skills of adaptability and flexibility through process can help us to be more responsive to stress. In other words, when life hands us something we don't like or reminds us of our past, we are quite literally able to take a breath and not let our old, wounded patterns drive our behavior or our emotional world. Dr. Viktor Frankl, survivor of the Holocaust and legend in the field of modern psychology for his work on meaning, and fellow existentialist Dr. Rollo May often spoke to this phenomenon. In his 1975 book, *The Courage to Create,* May asserted: "Human freedom involves our capacity to pause between stimulus and response and, in that pause, to choose the one response towards which we wish to throw our weight."[10]

How will you respond when faced with the stimulus of stress that is inevitable in this theater of life? No one expects you to be perfect at it. I am certainly still a work in process when it comes to responding instead of reacting. I challenge you to embrace the practices in this process as a rehearsal and training ground.

---

[10] May, R. (1975). *The Courage to Create*. New York: W.W. Norton, p. 100.

PRACTICE ONE

RESPONDING TO THE EDGE IN YOGA POSES

A common refrain that yoga teachers often hear from would-be students is, "I can't do yoga. I'm not flexible." We generally respond that physical flexibility is not a prerequisite for practicing yoga. Rather, engaging in consistent practice over time can help you to build flexibility, both physical and mental. Moreover, practicing physical poses in yoga is never about the poses themselves. As we teach in the yogic lineage in which I study, the purpose of engaging in yoga poses on a mat is to place us in laboratory conditions.

How we respond to discomfort, mental chatter, or approaching our edge on a yoga mat is a metaphor for how we may respond in life. In this practice, we will be working with one of the core poses of Hatha yoga, mountain pose, to play with this idea. You do not specifically need a yoga mat for this practice although if you have one you are invited to use it.

- Come to the front of your mat or to a place on the floor where you feel strong in your stance. Keep your feet together. If this puts too much pressure on your knees or hips, modify by stepping the feet apart slightly while maintaining your balance.
- Press down into your feet and extend up through the crown of your head. Keep your eyes open and look straight ahead.

- Bring your hands into prayer position in front of your chest. To engage the energetic potential of the pose even more, become firm through your buttocks and inner thighs and drop the tailbone.
- As you inhale, extend your arms straight overhead, interlacing your fingers into a temple-style position if possible. If this is not available in your body, keep the arms straight overhead, palms facing each other, shoulder distance apart. Do your best to keep the arms alongside your ears and slightly back.
- Use your breath to help you support the holding of the pose. This is not a contest to see how long you can hold the pose. Rather, when you first notice that you want to come out of it, challenge yourself to use your breath and other tools you now have to help you sustain the pose. In some yoga traditions, I've heard it said, when you want to come out of the pose, that's when the pose truly begins.
- Remember that the purpose of an edge is never to strive or push through pain. Always honor your body and back off when you need to.
- Reset and try again if possible. Sometimes the lesson we can learn in doing this type of work is that I can practice adaptability by taking a break, resetting my breath, and then trying again.

MODIFICATION NOTES:

- ✓ You are free to use the wall or a chair for support if you need to. You can stand up and come up against the wall for that extra support. If using a chair, you can stand behind the chair and hold on with one hand, and do your best to use the other hand and arm for the overhead component of the pose.
- ✓ If you are not able to stand, feel free to modify the spirit of this pose as needed from a sitting position. Press down wherever you can in your lower body, and bring the upper body into position as you are able.
- ✓ Feel free to use the following photographs as a guide.
- ✓ You can repeat this same general approach with coaching about the holds and the edge with any yoga pose that may currently be in your practice. Remember, the point is to notice if you respond or react when the intensity begins to build.

MOUNTAIN POSE VARIATIONS

Mountain Pose

Mountain Pose with Temple Arms

PRACTICE TWO

PLAYLIST SHUFFLE

In the practices on Distress Tolerance (Process Three) we discussed the power of listening to songs you don't like as powerful way to build this skill. There are so many metaphors that can be practiced through listening to music in various ways, and that spirit continues in this practice.

- Pull up one of the playlists you have already made for your work in this book. You also have the option of using another playlist on your phone or in your music collection.
- Put the playlist on shuffle and set an intention to listen through the whole playlist from start to finish, committing to not skip any tracks.
- You can dance along to the playlist if you wish, or simply engage in mindful listening.
- Notice whatever you notice about the process and feel free to take some of your insights to your journal when complete.

MODIFICATION NOTES:

- ✓ If you are using a CD player, you likely have access to the shuffle feature on that technology as well.
- ✓ If you do not have access to music on your smartphone, computer, or a CD player, you can always adapt by using the radio. Pick a station and commit to listening for a certain period of time, moving to or listening to whatever comes up.

PRACTICE THREE

TAKE IT TO THE PAGE–RANDOM DRAW EDITION

This version of take it to the page will come with a bit of a random twist. This will help you "go with" the idea of working with whatever you are given. There are several types of media that you can use to "draw" your word or phrase that will be your prompt for this practice. Several options are presented here, and these also serve as the Modification Notes for this practice.

- **OPTION 1:** Get out a book or magazine that you may have hanging around your house. Try to select a book that you have not yet read. Open to any random page and notice what the first word or phrase is that catches your attention. Write it down in your journal.
- **OPTION 2:** Go online and without giving it too much thought, click on a webpage that you may have bookmarked in your browser. Once you pull up that webpage, scroll down a bit without looking and then see what word or phrase catches your attention first. Write it down in your journal.
- **OPTION 3:** Use any junk mail sent to your place of residence. Open it up and notice the first word or phrase you see. Write it down in your journal.

- Set the timer for 5-10 minutes and use the word or phrase that caught your attention as your prompt. You can respond in any way you see fit: free writing, poetry, short story, a short scene, or a combination of forms.
- You may go longer than 10 minutes if you need the time, although I challenge you to make 5-10 minutes your minimum for this practice.

PRACTICE FOUR

GUSH ART– NON-DOMINANT HAND EDITION

Just notice what came up for you when you read the title of this practice. I generally hear a lot of, "I can't draw with my left hand" (in right handed folks) or, "No way can I work with my right hand" (from left handed folks). A primary aim of this practice is to notice any initial resistance and then go with it anyway, noticing whatever you may notice.

- Get out whatever materials you normally use for gush art.
- Set the timer for a minimum of 10 minutes.
- Challenge yourself to work only with your non-dominant hand and be open to whatever the process reveals. If you catch yourself getting frustrated or reactive, can you step back for a moment, resetting and taking a breath, and then return to the challenge at hand (pun intended).
- Notice whatever you notice. At the end of the time period, be sure to sit back, breathe, and notice what you just expressed, without analyzing or judging it. If you want to share some of your reflections in your journal you may, or you may continue with more of a silent meditative process.

MODIFICATION NOTE:

- ✓ If you are truly ambidextrous or have taught yourself to write with both hands, use the hand that you write with least for this practice.

GUSH ART–NON-DOMINANT HAND EXAMPLE

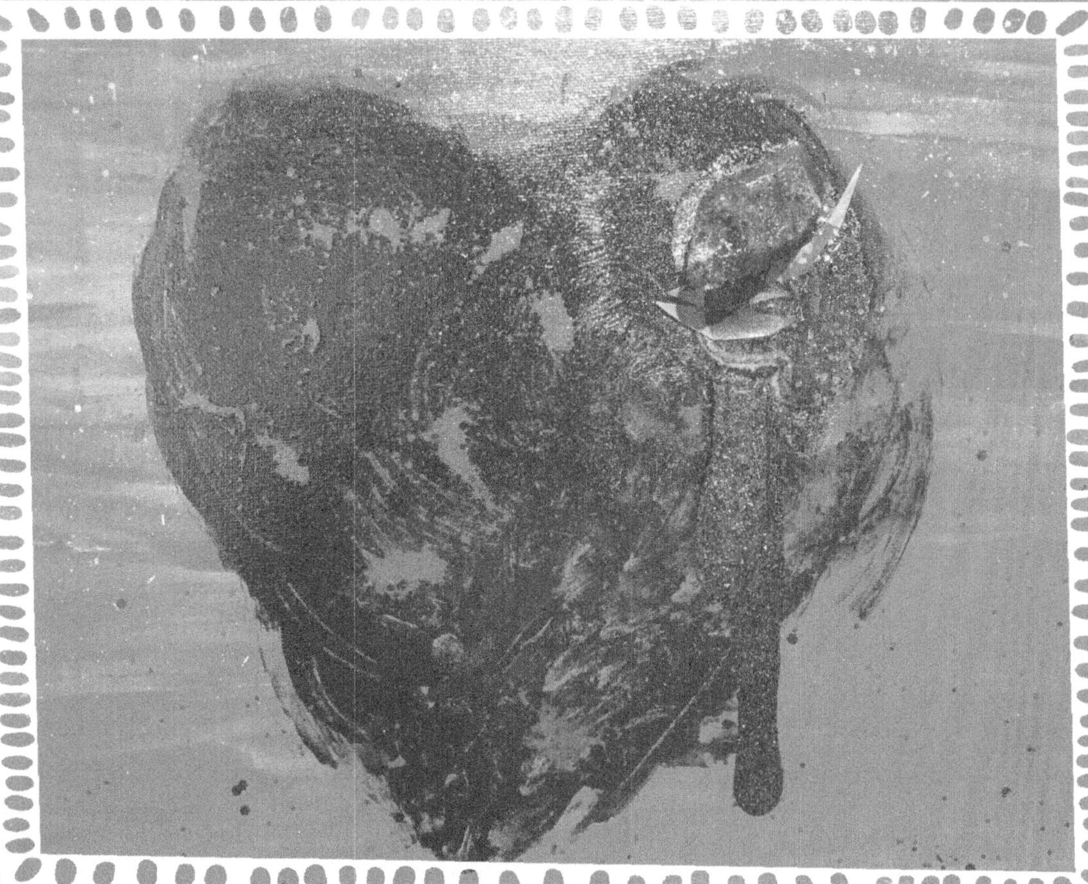

My Foolish Heart

~ DR. JAMIE (PRAGYA) **MARICH**
(One of my favorite pieces, completely "gushed" with my non-dominant hand)

PRACTICE FIVE

GUSH ART–ART MATERIALS ON THE EDGE

For many years, even as I allowed myself to begin exploring visual arts through media like collage and pastels, I never worked with paint. I saw paint as something that only "real" artists had a right to use and even though it was readily available in many of the craft stores that I frequented, I never bought it. Thanks to a former partner buying me a paint-by-numbers kit to give me an alternative to adult coloring pages, I began to discover the joy of playing with paint! The cover image that appears on the front of this book is fruit of the initial experiments I engaged in while working with this new channel for my expression.

- What is a visual medium that you have never worked in, or have worked in but consistently shy away from?
- Once you've identified the medium, you are challenged to work with it using whatever time is available to you. This may require going to the art/craft store or ordering online to obtain it.
- If you are not sure if there are mediums that you have avoided, go to the art/craft store or search online and investigate. I can still walk into my favorite craft store and find new things I haven't yet explored! Let the channel speak to you.
- Notice whatever you notice about how you react or respond to this practice.

MODIFICATION NOTES:

- ✓ If buying new materials isn't available to you, look around your living space and challenge yourself to work with whatever you have available. The key here is to use the channel that is most outside your comfort zone. So if you have a nubby golf pencil hanging around the house and have never dreamed of making "real art" with that, use the nubby golf pencil and embrace the challenge!
- ✓ Thrift stores are also an option. You may be surprised what you can discover in the realm of art materials you never dreamed of using.

PRACTICE SIX

PHOTODIALOGUE

In our final practice for this process, we continue with the theme of being adaptable and flexible to whatever the practice may reveal. In the instructions, I will give you some prompts for allowing photographs to select you instead of you deliberately choosing photographs. The instructions assume that we have an ample supply of pictures on smartphones, although the Modification Notes provide some other options if such pictures aren't available to you.

- In your photos on your smartphone, pull up the seventh to the last picture that you took. Resist any impulse to use another picture, even if this one feels like it isn't the greatest picture.
- Set the timer for 5 minutes. Take a breath and take in this image. What message might this image have for you today? Use the time and free write that photo's message for you. If a specific message doesn't seem relevant, you can also write about what you feel when you observe that photo.
- Now, scroll back to the oldest picture that you have saved on your phone. Again, resist any temptation to use another picture.

- Set the timer for 5 minutes. Take a breath and take in this image. What message might this image have for you today? Use the time and free write that photo's message for you. If a specific message doesn't seem relevant, you can also write about what you feel when you observe that photo.
- Now set the timer for 10 minutes. Allow these two images, or their inherent messages, to engage in dialogue with each other. When paired, the images may feel random. Just go with it, and notice what your writing process reveals.

MODIFICATION NOTES:

✓ If you don't have a smartphone with pictures but you can go online, go to your favorite search engine and type in "Images." Literally work with the first two images that come up.

✓ You may also work with images from your own personal photographs hanging around your living quarters. If you have old photo books, try to do a random draw, opening to any page of one book. Choose another book for the second picture.

✓ In any variation of this exercise, pictures of people or places may come with some emotional charge. Remember to use the other tools that you have developed in the practices and processes of this book, as you need to for support.

REFLECTION QUESTIONS FOLLOWING ADAPTABILITY AND FLEXIBILITY

- Describe your personal experience with the process.

- What did you discover in your process?

- What did you learn about yourself in the process?

- What did you notice about judgment or self-criticism during the process?

- What role did the multi-modality of the art forms play in discovering what you discovered in your process?

- Which of the skills explored in this process can be applied to your overall trauma recovery or wellness plan?

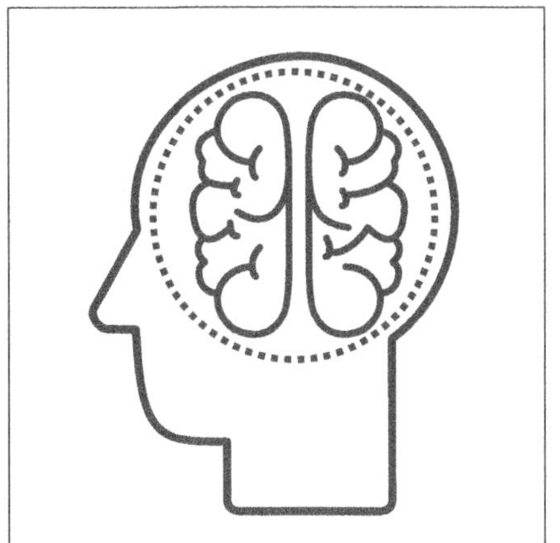

Process twelve

NOURISHMENT

What images or associations come up for you when you hear the word nourishment? For most of us in Western cultures, our association likely goes to food first. We eat to sustain life, to nourish ourselves. You may have heard health coaches or dieticians squabble about which foods are most nourishing to human bodies, or give their opinions about what gets in the way of true nourishment.

But is nourishment only about food and eating? And does food and eating have many insights to teach us about what it means to nourish our total selves—body, mind, and spirit? Let's break down the word to find out.

Nourish is middle English in origin and generally means "to feed." However, I invite you to look in any dictionary and notice how this concept of being fed plays out in all dimensions of experience, not just physically. In my favorite dictionary, I found these three simple definitions:

- To sustain with food; supply with what is necessary for life, health, and growth
- To cherish, foster, keep alive
- To strengthen, build up, or promote

I don't think a dictionary search has ever given me the chills as much as this one. These definitions help me realize that there is more than just my body to keep alive and healthy!

What do you notice as you consider the meaning of the word nourishment and its significance to your journey right now?

I first introduced the concept of nourishment in Process Four on Self-Compassion. While self-compassion is a buzzword in modern day mindfulness circles, to be frank, I prefer the concept of self-nourishment. To me, nourishment includes compassion toward the self. However, nourishment is a much more holistic term. When I think of nourishing myself, I picture giving myself a great big hug and bringing in all my internal and external resources. These not only help to keep me alive and well; they help me to live my fullest and most meaningful life.

Learning to fully nourish myself in all dimensions of my experience has been a true work in process and I'm happy to share with you some of what I've learned. You may feel that you still have a great deal to discover in this area, and that's okay. We all need to start somewhere. I can assure you that cultivating the skill of self-nourishment is one of the most precious gifts you can learn to give yourself in the journey of ongoing recovery, growth, and wellness.

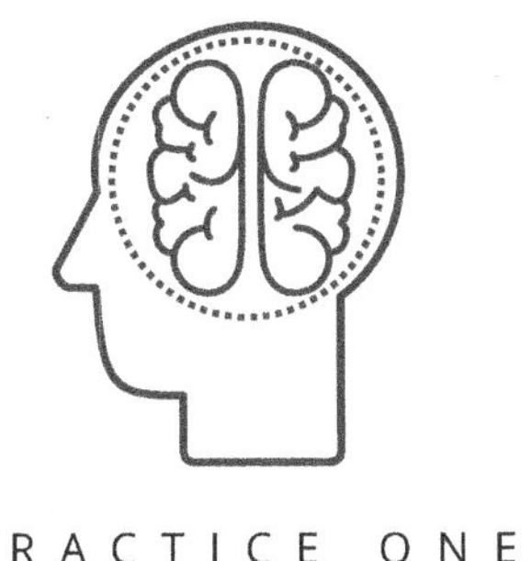

PRACTICE ONE

REVISITING THE NOURISHMENT AND DEPLETION INVENTORY

In Process Four, I introduced the Nourishment and Depletion Inventory. In this practice, we revisit this inventory. But, don't yet look back at what you did in Process Four; this comes in steps, so please be patient.

- The aim of this practice is for you to create a new Nourishment and Depletion Inventory now that you have engaged in many more processes and practices!
- Spend 1-2 minutes in mindful breathing. Consider setting an intention to write freely without censoring yourself or judging your experience. No one has to see this inventory besides you.
- Take out a piece of paper or go to a blank page in your journal. Make a line down the middle to create two columns on the page. If you are in a journal or notebook, you can use two full pages that face each other.
- On the left side column, take about 5 minutes to write down the people, places, things, and activities in your life that nourish you. If the word nourish is tricky for you, look it up in the dictionary for some additional inspiration. My general working definition of nourishment is to be fed, physically, emotionally, and spiritually, with little or no rebound experienced in terms of negative consequences.

- On the right side of the column, take the next 5 minutes to write down the people, places, things, and activities in your life that deplete you. As with your Nourishment and Depletion Inventory in Process Four, be mindful that some of the same people, places, things, and activities may appear in both columns. This often happens when you list children or close family members. It is more than okay to have something, someone, or someplace appear on both sides of the column. If they do, try to be more specific about what aspects of them are nourishing and what aspects are depleting.
- When you are done, give yourself a few minutes to breathe and center before looking over your list. Any surprises or new discoveries showing up?
- NOW you can look back to your inventory from Process Four. Has anything changed? Has anything remained the same? Any additional insights emerge from reading them side-by-side? Feel free to write down any gut level reactions in your journal.

MODIFICATION NOTES:

- ✓ If you are concerned about someone you live with or who is in your close space finding this inventory (especially if they appear on it), know that you can destroy the list as soon as you compose it and examine it. You can run it through a shedder, burn it, or tear it up into little pieces and flush it down the toilet. The important part is that you set an intention to internalize what you discovered in the practice before moving on with the process.
- ✓ If you struggle with verbalizing words on a page, drawing in symbols or images is also permissible, although the third practice in this chapter will take you into fuller exploration with visual components.

PRACTICE TWO

NOURISH YOURSELF WITH EXPRESSIVE ARTS

The invitation in this practice is quite simple. I used it as a bonus practice in Process Four. Here, I am directly working it into the process. I feel very strongly that learning to do this is vital to MANIFESTING continuing growth and care, the purpose of this section of the book.

- Review your list. Notice the expressive arts practices that showed up on the nourishing side of the inventory.
- Make some time in the next 48 hours to engage in that practice or those practices, especially if they not have been covered in the scope of this book.
- Keep in mind that there is no need to limit yourself to just one practice—in the spirit of expressive arts, if you have several listed, engage in the combination.
- Spend some time in your journal writing, artmaking, or a combination of the two to reflect upon your experiences.

MODIFICATION NOTE:

✓ If for some reason 48 hours isn't possible, commit to a time in the coming week or month. Actually schedule it into your calendar if you need to!

PRACTICE THREE

VIRIDITAS–THE GREENING POWER OF GOD

St. Hildegard of Bingen, a 12th century German mystic, healer—and in my opinion, one of our first expressive arts therapists—used a concept called viriditas in her healing ministry. Viriditas literally means "the greening power of God." Through my own study while on a retreat pilgrimage to Bingen in 2016, I learned that when a patient came to Hildegard, she approached health inventory through this lens of viriditas.

What is cutting off the greening power in your own life? Think about what trees need to flourish—water, sunlight, good soil. Carrying this metaphor over to your own life, what do you need to flourish? In my own work, I have found it very helpful to play with the color green as I contemplate these questions.
I began my work in this area not being a particular fan of the color green. Now, I adore the color so much I have two Hildegard-inspired tattoos (including the word viriditas) in what has become my favorite shade of green.

- Using any medium for art (e.g., pastels, crayons, pencil drawing, collaging, painting), set an intention to play with the various shades of green.
- This is essentially a gush art experience; your only challenge is to use shades of green, experimenting with any combination of shading and blending that seems to fit.

- Breathe as you work with the medium, setting the timer for at least 10 minutes (although you may go longer). Notice what impact the breath has on your movement and what shows up on the page.
- After the piece feels complete, take a moment to notice. Write down in your journal any insights that emerged, especially about the power of greening and nourishment in your own life and what may be obstructing it for you from. We will work with this concept more in the next practice.

MODIFICATION NOTE:

✓ I truly encourage you to work with the color green in this practice, even if you don't like the color or there is some resistance around it. If, for some reason there is a powerful traumatic trigger around the color green due to an unprocessed incident or memory, you may elect to do this practice with another color that you describe as nourishing.

VIRIDITAS EXAMPLES

(Remember to go online for the color version of these since color is the focus of this practice)

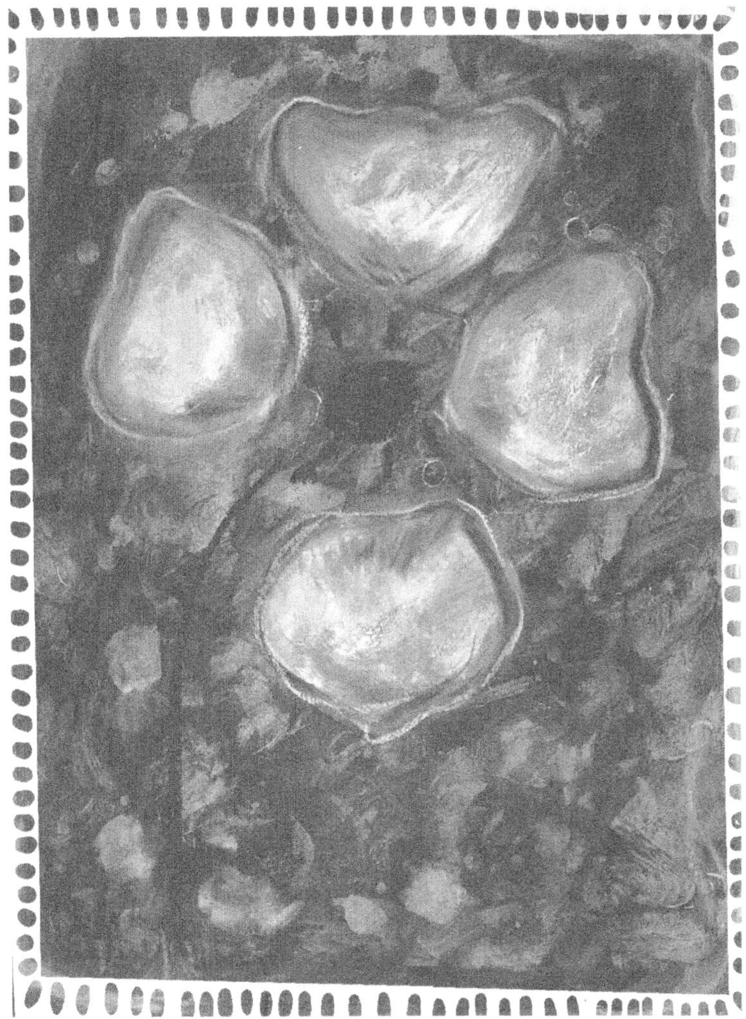

~ TRACEE **MOSS**

~ IRENE **RODRIGUEZ**

PRACTICE FOUR

LEARNING FROM *ARIDITAS*

In Latin, the opposite of *viriditas* is *ariditas;* being dried out and unable to grow. We get the English word arid from this root. In this practice you are invited to work with your inventory and any that you did with the previous three practices to further explore what keeps you arid, or cut off from the greening power of the divine, creative potential within you. If that language feels a little flowery, think of the teaching this way: What keeps you from nourishing yourself?

- After reviewing your inventory and other writing, take a few moments to breathe and notice. What image or series of images comes up for you that represents *ariditas*, or being dried out?
- Using any art materials at your disposal, bring a visual representation of *ariditas* to life. You may choose to draw your image, or use collaging to bring together several images. Other visual representations are also possible; go with the flow of your practice.
- Take a moment to breathe and notice what you experience in your body when you take in the piece that you just created. Go to your journal to free write on some of what you are noticing. If *ariditas* elicits a certain sensation in your body that does not feel healthy or in the service of your highest good, what practices or measures of care from the nourishing side of your inventory can help bring you back to life?

MODIFICATION NOTE:

- ✓ If nothing comes to you visually for ariditas, I challenge you to do a word chain on it (refer to Process Seven, Practice 1).

PRACTICE FIVE

INFUSING WITH GREENING POWER

Now that you have a better sense of what may block you from realizing the greening power in your own life, I invite you to set an intention of bringing more of that greening power back into your life. In this practice, we set our intention visually and notice what comes up.

- Take a look at the expressive art piece that you just created on *ariditas*. Ask yourself, how would I approach infusing this piece with greening power?
- Bring out your green art making materials and just go with it. Allow yourself to move with breath and transform the piece as you are internally guided.
- Notice what happens, being mindful not to force or strive for any outcome.

MODIFICATION NOTES:

✓ You may decide to duplicate your ariditas piece and then engage in this practice, creating a side-by-side effect.

✓ If you engaged in the Word Chain alternative in the previous practice, use the color green to begin drawing doodles or streams of color around the words. Then, challenge yourself to create a new word chain beginning with the word viriditas.

PRACTICE SIX

FOOD AS EXPRESSIVE ARTS

This is the perfect chapter to touch upon the healing of food and the practices of cooking and baking as expressive arts. You can engage in this practice at a variety of levels. You may not fancy yourself much of a cook. I always laugh when I think of something that James Stafford, my long-time musical collaborator, said to me: "Jamie, I don't cook. I warm food."

You may come into this practice like James, or you may be a candidate to receive a Michelin star for your culinary wizardry. The key is that you approach this practice in a mindful way—using your preparation of food and the consumption of it as a vehicle for staying meditative and connected to the moment.

- Set an intention to prepare a meal. Any meal will work for this practice. If you don't have a dish in mind, consider finding a recipe and working from those directions.
- If possible, try to select fresh ingredients so that you can approach every aspect of it—the chopping of vegetables, the cracking of eggs, and the measuring of liquids as an opportunity to practice mindfulness.
- Employ all 5 of your senses as you prepare the meal—what smells are you aware of as you prepare? What are the textures you notice as you work with ingredients? What tastes are apparent as you sample your

work along the way? What are you noticing visually about the food and how it transforms? What sounds accompany the preparation of the meal?

- After the meal is prepared, set an intention to eat it mindfully. For me, this means savoring every aspect of the experience. Take a moment to really look at your creation, maybe even snapping a quick picture of it. Smell what you prepared overall and know that you can smell each individual bite before you bring it up to your mouth to taste it. Notice the sounds as the utensils make contact with the food. Notice your hands touching the utensils or any food that you touch directly (e.g., bread).
- Take your time, and notice whatever you notice. If you feel led to journal or to draw about your reflections from this practice, please feel free to do that.

MODIFICATION NOTES:

- ✓ If you are absolutely stuck when it comes to cooking or baking, you are free to engage in this practice by going to one of your favorite restaurants. Order a dish that you find particularly nourishing and engage in this second part of the practice.
- ✓ I want to emphasize that even if your best culinary talent is "warming food," that can still work for this practice. Perhaps consider getting ingredients for a salad as an a starting point. You can still engage in the spirit of this practice with that simple start.
- ✓ **BONUS PRACTICE:** Based on this experience, what foods feel like they are the most nourishing to your body going forward? If you can't specifically think of foods, notice what colors are most apparent to you as nourishing. Are there any foods in this general group of colors that you know, either from experience or recommendations from professionals, are especially healthy for you? Consider making a collage of these foods or drawing them and place this creation somewhere near where you prepare food.

REFLECTION QUESTIONS FOLLOWING NOURISHMENT

- Describe your personal experience with the process.
- What did you discover in your process?
- What did you learn about yourself in the process?
- What did you notice about judgment or self-criticism during the process?
- What role did the multi-modality of the art forms play in discovering what you discovered in your process?
- Which of the skills explored in this process can be applied to your overall trauma recovery or wellness plan?

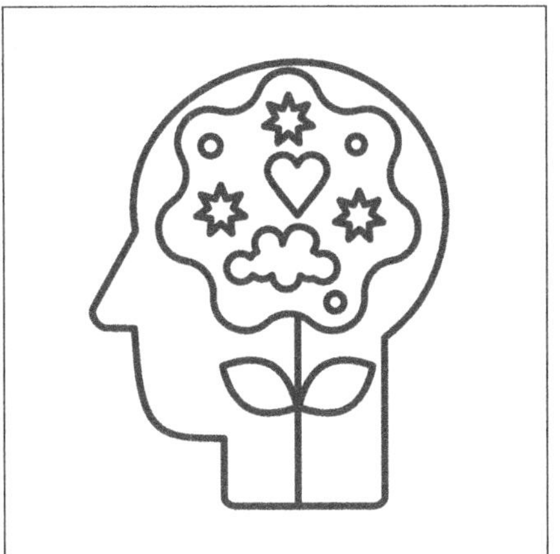

Process thirteen

DAILY PRACTICE

When I was a kid growing up, *practice* had a negative connotation. Although I grew to love music in my own way, younger Jamie resented having to practice her violin every day. Hearing my mom say, "Jamie, time to practice!" never failed to grate on my body and soul like nails on a chalkboard.

I was not one of those kids who loved and craved music. I took lessons because I felt my parents were making me. I eventually grew to enjoy playing the violin and love playing the guitar, but those early experiences with practice were not positive. I always schemed to get away with as little practice as possible. As I entered my teenage years I started to enjoy playing my instruments more.

What I was scratching out no longer sounded like noise; it sounded like music. Then I started to make the connection that practice is required for competence and growth.

When I became acquainted with meditation and yoga in my twenties, I initially found it curious that the word *practice* was used so frequently. In holistic circles, it's common to hear the phrase "we practice yoga" or "my daily meditation practice," because they are just that—practices. They are a series of techniques, strategies, tools, and other activities that lead us to our highest selves that must be practiced to be developed and become internalized. The reward for daily practice is not necessarily competence; to me there is no such thing as a professional yogi, a professional meditator, or a professional practitioner of the expressive arts.

The payoff of daily practice is an ever-increasing sense of life mastery. While I learned this phrase *life mastery* from my teacher Yogi Desai, for me the phrase is very open to interpretation and discussion. Life mastery is not about winning at life or being successful and a master in your own mind. Rather, life mastery is an enhanced sense of being able to *respond,* rather than react, to what life brings your way. You develop an increased awareness to use your skills to help you alleviate the presence of suffering in your life caused by old reactive patterns. If life brings you more stress, suffering, or wounding (which life inevitably does), you become better prepared to handle it.

To cultivate life mastery, daily practice is required. One of my favorite expressive artists, Kirtan singer and teacher Krishna Das, frequently shares in his talks that it doesn't matter what your daily practice is, as long as you have one. His daily practice is sitting at his harmonium and singing, which he has described as vital for clearing out the dark corners of his heart. He further explained that some days he doesn't feel like it, and yet he does it anyway, so aware is he of its importance.

Your daily practice can be singing, writing, dancing, painting, drawing, receiving images/photography, cooking, chopping wood, or playing with your animals. Your daily practice may even be a combination of these activities.

Whatever you can engage in consistently that leads you home to the present moment when you notice your mind wandering away or into obsessive, destructive patterns becomes a candidate for daily practice. In the Yoga Sutras of Patanjali, the sacred texts that codified the ancient art of yoga, practice becomes well-grounded when we engage in it with devotion over a long period of time.[11] There is no fast track.

My daily practice ebbs and flows with the seasons of my life although I always have a daily set of activities in which I engage to get me into my breath and body and out of my racing mind. In the morning, I generally read from two spiritual books, breathe, say a set of prayers, practice some yoga asana or improvisational movement. I tend to like it quiet in the morning so if time permits I usually add an extended sitting meditation practice or walking meditation into the mix. In the evening before I go to sleep is when I add the music in, taking some time to dance, engage in a more extended yoga asana sequence, paint, or play around with video editing. My practice does not look the same day-to-day or week-to-week. The only constant is that I am doing something daily for my own wellness.

In the two practices that follow, you are challenged to explore what works for you in terms of building a daily practice. You may already have a very consistent one in which case this process will help you to evaluate and to fine tune. If you are not sure if you have a daily practice or are just starting to think about developing one, you are in the right place!

Unlike many of the other practices in the book, these next two are not designed to be done in one sitting. You are invited to work with each practice over a period of about 5-7 days. While you can work with several of the practices together, the key is that you give each at least this amount of time to observe and notice your experiences with it. This laboratory of practice is designed to help you discover what will work for you as you build your daily practice.

---

[11] Satchidananda, S. (2017). *The Yoga Sutras of Patanjali*, 6th Printing. Buckingham, VA; Integral Yoga Publications

PRACTICE ONE

MESSAGES FROM THE SKY

This practice is inspired by one of my dear friends and collaborative professional partners, Dr. Steve Dansiger. Almost every day, Steve posts a picture of the sky on social media, whether it's from his own home or on the road. While I tease him that it's part of his signature social media style, I've come to appreciate the beauty in the practice of receiving an image from some element in nature consistently. There is also space to write reflections accordingly based on how the sky may speak to you energetically.

- For your first time engaging in the practice, the simple invitation is to take a picture of the sky above you wherever you are. You may decide that you are going to take (receive) an image each morning for several consecutive days, or maybe the evening works better for you. You are free to receive several images throughout the day, based on the location and the impact that the sky has on you at any given time.
- The point of this practice is not to receive the most beautiful images of the sky, rather, to record a moment during your day and work with its power in other practices like written reflection. After you receive the image, take a breath and notice if a message is coming to you, or maybe a poem will flow.

- All the practices in this process encourage you to engage in a practice for at least five days in a row and notice what you notice, recording your reflections in your smartphone camera (if that is available) or on a traditional camera. Be sure to keep your journal handy so that you can work with the interplay between the images and the messages that you may receive.
- After five days, notice the spread of your images together or notice if your written reflections on those images hold a common theme. That theme may come with a vital message for your life and your practice right now.

MODIFICATION NOTES:

✓ You are able to use photo filters on your smartphone for this practice, especially if it helps to better describe the experience you are having in real time.

✓ Perhaps another nature element works better for you, like a certain tree or a rock that looks different depending on the weather or the time of day. I like using the sky because I can look up, wherever I am, and it's always there. Receiving these images can teach us powerful lessons about the flow between consistency and change.

✓ If you travel frequently or you are traveling over the course of this 5-day practice, consider observing your received image in Place #1 and compare it to your image of the sky in Place #2. What do the skies in each place have to say to each other? What do they have to say to you? Allow this to guide some of your written inquiry.

MESSAGES FROM THE SKY EXAMPLES

~ SAM **ORTEGO**

~ OLA **SOBANSKI**

One

(a poem corresponding with the sunset pictures from Florida above)

The earth and sky are one
Just as Jesus and Hanuman are One
How could one ever go back to sleep
After being this awakened?

How could anyone hear their name
Shouted in anger again
When they've finally heard it
Whispered with such love.

The earth and sky are one
Just as Jesus and Hanuman are One
The truth finally found me
May I never get lost again

~ DR. JAMIE (PRAGYA) **MARICH**

Georgia Power Sunrise

~ DR. STEPHEN **DANSIGER**

Reflections from the Sky

The news of his death took my breath away.
No words found my heart or mind . . .
just a void. An empty space where
his larger than Life
Physical presence once resided.

The silence gave way to
a gasp of air . . . that gave
birth to tears of loss and sadness
. . . and pain.

I suddenly was without a container to hold my feelings.
My ground had fallen from beneath me and all that remained
was a well of grief and a desire to lay in the floor covered in my tears.

I asked to be held.
I asked to be rocked.
I asked for prayers for the family.
I asked for prayers for me so that I could find my foundation once more, and offer solace with a wide container to bear the grief and sooth lamenting hearts.

My dragon nature rose up
within me and asked for fire.
Fire to purify and to warm my soul.
I sat in the heat and booked a flight to the mountains of Colorado.
The ceremonial sacred fire called me.
I answered the call as I sequestered myself in front of the fire
watching the flames dance as my tears released from there frozen slumber.

I slept in front of the fire and asked for strength.
I journeyed to the Colorado Mountains praying
before the fire for my dear friend to go forward
to the eternal light.

The fire asked me to stay and slumber under the star lit sky.
The fire asked me to trust the Great Spirit that had called my friend's soul home.

I said yes and let the fire and stars dance life back into my heart.

~ DR. KELLIE **KIRKSEY**

PRACTICE TWO

DAILY YOGA ASANA PRACTICE

Devoted practitioners of yoga generally feel a deficit in their bodies if they go a day without practicing yoga *asanas,* or poses. While the full practice of yoga involves more than just *asanas* (ethics, breath practices, and meditative principles are of utmost importance), in this practice you are invited to focus primarily on asanas and working with these other limbs as you feel called.

- If you already have an existing yoga practice, my invitation for you is to practice for 5 days consistently. The time of the day you practice is up to you. Many people swear by morning practice, whereas I enjoy doing my extended asana and meditation practice before bed. The amount of time you spend in your practice is up to you, although I would advise at least 15–20 minutes of poses.
- If you have little or no experience in the practice of yoga, going to a live class is your best introduction. Go on your search engine and seek out yoga classes in your local area, taking great care to notice if the studio feels accessible and welcoming to you and if there are classes appropriate for beginners. If you are not sure, call the studio manager/owner and ask. I recommend trying at least 5–6 yoga classes before making a definitive judgment. See if you can apply what you are learning in the classes into your daily life in the days after you attend.

- If classes aren't accessible to you or you need a review, feel free to visit my trauma-informed *Yoga Unchained* series developed with Jessica Sowers. In working with this process of daily practice, you can consider focusing on one or two poses each day before doing the whole sequence. You can access the video series here: **www.traumamadesimple.com/pnp**

MODIFICATION NOTES:

- ✓ While the *Yoga Unchained* videos interweave many modifications, you may feel more comfortable doing a chair yoga class or sequence. There are many quality chair yoga instructors accessible on YouTube. My favorite is Emily Wells of Wells Therapeutics. Tai chi master Don Fiore is another well-known YouTube personality that can lead you gently through this related movement practice.
- ✓ If the physical postures of yoga do not feel accessible at all to you right now, you are free to do daily practice with the breath strategies only. You can also access these on the online supplemental site for further instruction: **www.traumamadesimple.com/pnp**
- ✓ **BONUS PRACTICE:** Consider journaling after each daily yoga/asana practice and document your reflections, specifically what you are learning about yourself as you encounter the pose.

PRACTICE THREE

TUNING THE DAILY INSTRUMENT

This practice is a bit of a throwback to my early childhood days of practicing an instrument. As I described earlier, although I didn't like it at the time, I learned some of my most salient lessons about the power of practice during these years. In this practice, you are invited to play an instrument for the next seven days as part of your daily practice. Fret not—if your first instinct is, "But I don't play an instrument," I have plenty of ideas for you!

- If you play a musical instrument, my invitation to you is to set aside dedicated time (15–20 minutes each day) to play it. If you are a regular musician and you already do this, I challenge you to continue to engage in this practice with more meditative intent. If you play an instrument and don't get to it as often as you like, now is your chance to explore how playing for the joy of playing impacts your daily practice.
- If you are not specifically skilled at playing an instrument, consider using the natural instrument of your voice! Pick a song each day to sing along to, and know that there are thousands of karaoke and backing tracks on YouTube and the various musical streaming services. What would it feel like if you deliberately sang for seven days in a row?

- Another natural option is to drum. You can sit down and drum against your thighs with your hands or drum on the table or another surface. My advice is to start slow and work your way up to faster beats, being mindful of your breath and bodily responses. If you notice yourself getting too activated or stressed, take some time to catch your breath and back off the intensity.

MODIFICATION NOTE:

✓ While you are free to modify this practice in any way that may work for you, my clear invitation is that you just give this a try! If your initial resistance or inclination is, "I'm not a good singer," let me assure you, that doesn't matter. The important thing, as it relates to this practice, is that you use your voice.

PRACTICE FOUR

DAILY GUSH ART PAGES

In her classic work *The Artist's Way,* Julia Cameron describes the classic practice of morning pages. No matter how you are feeling when you wake up in the morning, she challenges you to write three full pages, no inhibitions. Like with many of the practices we've visited in this book, quality of outcome is not the intention with morning pages. When I went through The Artist's Way, the pages helped me to get my stuff out so it wasn't clogging my flow for the rest of the day. In this practice, I will invite you into a similar practice but instead of using the written word, I am proposing that you use gush art.

- For the next 7 days, commit to creating three full pages of gush art each morning, using whatever materials are available to you.
- I invite you not to do any big written reflections on the gush art pages for the days in these practices. Use the gush art as the practice itself.
- At the end of the 7 days, you are invited into writing. The objective of this writing is not to engage in any heavy analysis about what you created. Rather, reflect upon how you feel at the time of writing because of having engaged in the gush art practice. Did you notice or observe anything different about the flow of your day?

MODIFICATION NOTE:

- ✓ Three pages is suggested as a minimum based on Julia Cameron's inspiration from *The Artist's Way*. If working on the same canvas throughout the week or on the same collage feels like a better fit, that's a workable modification. My suggestion for this option is that you set the timer for a minimum of ten minutes each day to guide your work and challenge you to commit to a certain period.

PRACTICE FIVE

DAILY *DANCING MINDFULNESS*

For me, *Dancing Mindfulness* is not merely a class or a program that I created—it's a way of life and a daily practice. I dance mindfully in one way or another every day, whether I put a formal playlist together and move in my home studio, or dance through the kitchen or around my office. In this practice, I invite and challenge you to dance at least once a day for the next seven days. Here are some ideas to get you started:

- Remember that *Dancing Mindfulness* experiences can vary in length. You can dance to one song or to an entire playlist. Pick a length that will be feasible for you to practice each day, even if you are practicing a full hour on day one and only can manage a song or two on all the other days. One song is better than no songs!
- The music you use is completely up to you. Use playlists you've made already throughout your working in this book or see what new tunes YouTube or your favorite streaming service can offer you.
- Perhaps play around with dancing at different times during the day. Maybe even experiment with dancing when you are feeling pretty chill and then dancing when you are feeling stressed out. What do you notice?

- At the end of the seven days, journal some of your reflections about what you learned about yourself and embracing this practice of daily dancing.

MODIFICATION NOTE:

✓ While you are free to modify this practice in any way that may work for you, please just give this a try! If your first resistance or inclination is that "I'm not a good dancer," let me assure you, that doesn't matter. The important thing, as it relates to this practice, is that you move your body in whatever way you are safely able to move your body today.

PRACTICE SIX

DAILY PRACTICE LOG

If you are reading ahead, I encourage you to save this practice until after you've done the other five. Now that you have a variety of ideas, both from this chapter and from other places in the book, on what you can do for daily practice, it's up to you to mix and match. The intention of this practice is to invite you into exploration and document your insights about what you discover.

- For the next 1-2 weeks, commit to engaging in some form of daily practice or practices. While you can work with a blend of meditative and spiritual techniques, I challenge you to work at least one expressive arts practice into your daily routine.
- Your practice or series of practices may look different from day-to-day. That's okay. The important thing is that you just practice.
- Before you go to sleep at the end of your day, document in your journal what practices you engage in that day. You can also note any observations or insights about your life or specifically how you handled yourself in life that day. Notice and document if any of your practices seemed to impact your ability to respond instead of react.
- At the end of the 1-2 week period, go back through the journal and notice what you notice. Do any patterns emerge? Are you developing any insights about what you know will best serve you in a daily practice going forward?

MODIFICATION NOTES:

- ✓ Documenting your insights through recording on audio or video also works as an alternative to journaling. When you reflect, listen to any changes in tone of voice each day. Are you noticing any connections between the enthusiasm in your voice and certain practices?
- ✓ **BONUS PRACTICE:** Consider crafting an updated *Poem of Instruction* (Process Four, Practice 5) after completing this daily practice log.

REFLECTION QUESTIONS FOLLOWING DAILY PRACTICE

- Describe your personal experience with the process.

- What did you discover in your process?

- What did you learn about yourself in the process?

- What did you notice about judgment or self-criticism during the process?

- What role did the multi-modality of the art forms play in discovering what you discovered in your process?

- Which of the skills explored in this process can be applied to your overall trauma recovery or wellness plan?

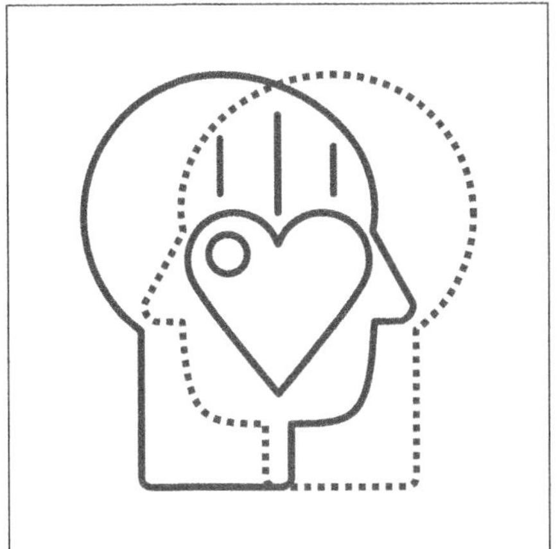

Process fourteen

BEYOND SELF-CARE

Self-care is one of the most used and yet often misunderstood terms in modern health care and wellness circles. Professionals are constantly being reminded to engage in acts of self-care to improve their health and longevity. Yoga studios and other wellness venues continually invite us through their doors to take better care of ourselves.

Sure, it can be lovely to treat ourselves to the finer things in life like pedicures, dance classes, and weekend retreats. However, actions are not genuine self-care and self-nourishment if we only do them every so often and then go back to the regular rat race of life. Moreover, if the purpose of engaging in this type of self-care is just to rejuvenate ourselves to go back into our lives to be more productive, then something vital is still missing. When our supposed self-care actions are not informed and motivated by the simple fact that it's our birthright to be gentle and kind to ourselves, we are in need of deeper nourishment.

In this section of the book, I've provided many ideas and hopefully some food for contemplation on how to better nourish yourself. In this process, I challenge you to take the fruits of what you've learned about nourishment and daily practice and use them to transform your way of life. My hope is that you will move beyond token actions of self-care that serve as mere respites from the stress of life and learn to truly cherish yourself as a divine being who deserves a more peaceful, less reactive lifestyle.

In a recent class, one of my yoga teachers, Eknath, invited us to "Be exquisitely gentle" with ourselves. When he issued this challenge, my face smiled, my heart danced, and I felt myself breathe a little deeper. It felt so good to receive this permission! Yet, I realized that I do not need this permission from an outside source. I move beyond self-care when I give myself permission to be gentle and nurturing and loving to the divine being that I am.

In this process, I invite you to work with strategies for moving beyond self-care. If the term self-care still works for you, feel free to use it. These days, I tend to prefer the terms self-nurturing or self-nourishment. Whatever terminology you embrace, my challenge for you is to use these practices to help you make it a way of life. I urge you to start seeing opportunities to be gentle with yourself in all areas of life. For instance, setting a boundary, saying no, or canceling plans may be a greater act of self-care than any pedicure or massage could ever be!

Releasing the attachments that bind you and keep you stuck in a reactive pattern could be the greatest work of self-preservation and personal growth in which you've ever engaged—leading to a healthier you and positively influencing those in your circles. Learning to nourish your expressive soul in small pockets, during the pauses you give yourself throughout the day, could be your deepest path to transformation.

Too often I see people stress themselves six days a week and maybe give themselves one day off for replenishment. While there is nothing inherently wrong with treating yourself to a vacation or something special if you have the means to do this, in this process I ask you to explore the idea of constantly being gentle to yourself. Such a process does not require a special occasion. This approach includes finding opportunities for refuge throughout every day, and making a commitment to releasing ourselves from the reactive patterns in our mind that keep us in our stressful loops.

Easier said than done, right?

Believe me, I've uttered this protest many times in my own healing journey, and I still say it from time to time when faced with a new challenge. However, I wouldn't be offering you this teaching if I hadn't personally experienced the power of its truth. These expressive arts practices will help guide you into the transition of moving beyond self-care.

PRACTICE ONE

CHANTING *OM*

Chanting the sound of *OM* is a well-known component of many yoga and meditation classes in the modern age. Even if you've never stepped foot inside of a yoga studio or a meditation space, mainstream television or movie exposure has likely given you some frame of reference for this sound. The typical image people associate with it is that of a blissed-out yogi chanting at the end of class, eye closed, hands in a perfect meditative gesture.

In this practice, I ask you to shift your perception a bit. In the Yoga Sutras of Patanjali (the first sage to write down the precepts of the ancient practice of yoga), OM is described as the vibration of the universe—the cosmic blend of all the sounds of the world coming together. When we chant this sound, we are chanting to our version of God/Higher Power/inner power that also dwells within each of us. Every chant of OM taps us into that cosmic source. In his commentary on the yoga sutras, Sri Swami Satchidananda states, "It is the seed from which all other sounds manifest. That is why OM represents God in the fullest sense. It has the power to create everything."[12]

- If you have never chanted OM before, it's important to find a space or a place where you feel safe enough to try this out for the first time.

---

[12] Satchidananda, S. (2017). *The Yoga Sutras of Patanjali*, 6th Printing. Buckingham, VA; Integral Yoga Publications

- Take an inhale, really noticing it, and as you exhale, allow the sound "OM" to be made. Notice it coming from your core and use the breath to support and extend it. If you start quietly, that's okay.
- Continue chanting OM as many times as feels appropriate. If the word "chant" is a block for you, just think of it as humming or singing.
- After your chanting is complete, take a moment to notice the impact and reverberation of the sound in your physical body. Notice what this means for you personally.
- To expand the practice, find various places throughout the day where you can chant the sound of OM. Maybe in your car on the way to work? When you wake up or before you go to bed? Replacing a smoke break? However you choose to work with the chant, consider that every time you chant this sound you are tapping into the divine source of life that lives within you!

MODIFICATION NOTES:

- ✓ For those of you who find this practice and the language I've used to describe it uncomfortable, know that you can take what you like and leave the rest. Try humming (a simple Hmmmm) and notice what you notice about the impact of that practice in your body and breath.
- ✓ For those of you who feel that this practice is at odds with your religious belief system, you can also try the humming method. Another option is to chant or sing a word that is meaningful in your faith tradition, like "Amen."

✓ If you have hearing loss or another condition that prevents you from vocalizing, you can move on to the next practices where I further work with the idea of the internal sound more somatically. You also have the option to find a recording of someone chanting OM (there are many available on the Internet) and come as close to the speakers as you are able, sensing into the vibration of the sound and noticing its impact on you. As with many practices in this book, it's more about the intention and pointing it to where you want the energy to flow. Do what you are able and notice the impact.

PRACTICE TWO

EMBODIED SOUND

Music is more than just sound you can hear with your ears. We feel music through vibrations that resonate in our bodies. In this practice, I invite you to stay in the spirit of OM or whatever sound you came to chant or sing in Practice 1. The intention here is to notice how you may experience sound in your body and then go with it! Practices 2 and 3 are ideally completed together so set aside enough time (20–25 minutes minimum). The same modification notes for Practice 1 apply here as well.

- Chant or sing the word OM, or any other workable alternative identified in the previous practice.
- After the chant, come into a place of stillness. Notice whatever you notice in your body. Are there any reverberations present in your body? Notice those sensations without over-analyzing them or trying too hard to describe them.
- Now repeat your chant three more times.
- Return to a place of stillness and notice what you notice. If the reverberation is strong in any one place such as your heart, your stomach, or your head, bring one or both of your hands there and notice the sensation.
- Repeat your chant three more times.

- Return to a place of stillness briefly and notice what you notice. Now, I invite you to respond to the needs of the body. Does your body need more stillness to sink into these sensations? Or is the sensation prompting you to move or sway?
- Repeat this practice as many times as you need to, being curious to how you experience sound within you.
- Go on to the next practice for working further with what you discovered in this practice.

PRACTICE THREE

RECEIVING THE MESSAGE

Nowadays, we are used to receiving messages in the form of texts or emails. It feels like the more technologically absorbed we become as a culture, the more cut off we can be from the internal messages that our bodies want to give us through sensation and vibration. This practice is a continuation of what you did in Practice 2, inviting you to deeply receive and reflect upon the messages of sound and vibration in your body.

- Have your art materials readily accessible.
- If you took a break between Practice 2 and now, allow yourself to complete Practice 2 again. After the last round of instructions in Practice 2, return here.
- Using the sensations in your body as a guide, allow yourself to express your experience using the art materials. Take as much time as you need. There is no objective or directive to this exercise, simply let sensation be your guide.
- After this part of the practice feels complete, take a moment to breathe and look at your creation with meditative awareness.

- Is there a verbal message that seems to be coming through as you look at your sensation-guided piece of art? If so, you can write it down in your journal and reflect in whatever way feels appropriate (e.g., free writing, poetry). You may even choose to write out a classic "text message" exchange between your internal divine as expressed through your body and your rational mind. The options are limitless.

MODIFICATION NOTES:

- ✓ You can do the free writing first if this feels more appropriate, although I discourage it. The aim of this exercise is for you to get more into your body and not rely so much on the analysis of the mind. Working with the art making before the writing is the ideal sequence to this practice.
- ✓ You can elect to skip the verbal portion of the exercise. The message you receive may not be able to formed into words—it may exist only at the level of sensation and visual art. The important thing is that you can put this artwork in a place where you can see it and be reminded of this experience, and the message it relays to you.

PRACTICE FOUR

DANCING WITH THE HEARTBEAT

In this practice, we continue to work with internal music and the inner wisdom of your experience. As we cultivate this practice and this process, may we come to realize that we have a beautiful and divine world living inside of us. When we feel stuck, all we need to do is access its wisdom. This practice may be one strategy that you find useful as an access point. Practices 4 and 5 complement each other so if you can create the time to do them together (20–30 minutes), please do so.

- For the first time trying this practice, come to a place that feels quiet enough and safe enough for you.
- Take a few breaths and feel the ground beneath you.
- Bring your dominant hand to your heart. Take a few moments to make contact with your pulse and allow yourself to feel the beating of the heart.
- After you've established this connection, allow your other hand to begin to move. You may notice that your whole body begins to move. That's great! Keep going with it but keep the dominant hand on the heart. Try to stay with this for at least 2–3 minutes, although you may go longer.

- Come to stillness, and notice the impact of your movement on the stillness. Take some deep breaths.
- Now, bring your non-dominant hand to your heart. Take a few moments to make contact with your pulse and allow yourself to feel the beating of the heart.
- After you've established this connection, allow your other hand to begin to move. You may notice that your whole body begins to move. Keep going with it but keep the non-dominant hand on the heart. Try to stay with this at least 2-3 minutes although you may go longer.
- Come to stillness, and notice the impact of your movement on the stillness. Take some deep breaths. Feel the ground beneath you.
- After you've developed more familiarity with this practice, try it in places where it does not feel quite so calm and quiet. Perhaps closing the door and doing it in your office space? Or in the kitchen when your house feels like it's about to explode in chaos. As I've advised many places in this book, just notice what you notice.

MODIFICATION NOTE:

✓ You are free to modify this practice in whatever manner you may need to physically. If you don't feel much of a pulse when you bring your hand to your heart, you can work with the pulse point on your wrist or behind your ears. If you do not have full use of the arms, respond by moving whatever parts of your body you are able, even if you are only able to respond to the heart beat with the rhythm of your breath.

PRACTICE FIVE

A LOVE LETTER TO MYSELF

In Process Six, Practice 6, I invited you to write a love letter to a part of your body. For those of us on a recovery path, especially one leading us out of internalized shame, this task was no small feat. Now that you have spent some more time growing in your expressive arts practice and recovery journey, I challenge you to write a letter to your entire being—body, mind, and spirit. If you notice some initial resistance to this challenge in your body, acknowledge it, breathe into it, and notice what happens. You can either wait for that sensation to pass, or use the energy it generates to move you into action with this practice.

- Take whatever time you need, using whatever writing materials you need, to craft this letter of love and appreciation to yourself.
- The letter can be as long or as short as you need it to be. In the content, be sure to use what you have learned about the importance of nourishing yourself, embracing the care of yourself as a serious vocation, and any other messages given to you by the expressive arts process.
- When you are through, feel free to share this letter with a trusted friend or member of your support system, or you can leave it in a strategic place where you can access and read it whenever you need to.

MODIFICATION NOTES:

- ✓ If writing is not easily available to you, please consider recording your love letter to yourself and listening to it.
- ✓ If words aren't quite coming to you, how would you express a love letter to the self visually?
- ✓ You also have the option of recording the love letter as a BONUS PRACTICE even if you did write it out.
- ✓ If this exercise feels super vulnerable for you right now, consider getting together with a friend or a trusted member of your support group to help you craft the letter. While it's important that they not write the letter for you, their support may be vital in your work with this practice.

A LOVE LETTER TO MYSELF EXAMPLES

Dear Honored Temple:

Hello that means speaking to myself in the first person. The Light I carry is within you. It burns passionately for me to make a meteorite impact in my human personified field that hits my soul: different abilities. Hello, my wisdom overwhelms me from-time-to-time, but it sheds perspective and change often in a society that is; rigid and molded in their thought processes. Yes, that means I blaze a path that has little trail work done. Met with fierce overriding emotions--*embrace the suck*--echoes in my conscious mind's ear.
My passionately felt emotions are permissive for the first time in my body at thirty-two years of age.

My honored temple: you came into this world sustaining big 'T' trauma. I loss oxygen at birth for a whole sixty seconds. Ultimately, resulting in Spastic Quadriparesis Cerebral Palsy with characteristics of Autism Spectrum Disorder. There have been moments where I let the black death of oxygen deprivation get me down, even as recently as, 2018. I am persistent. I have been given this great honor to live and make a difference, and to thwart it by ending my life sniffs out a fiercely burning bonfire.

Further, I am beginning to untangle confusion, "a confused mind says, no." In doing so, I must bare witness to and radically accept my limitations. I have the ability to empower many, yet having the wisdom that oxygen deprivation does cause increase limitations. My honored temple is being affected by this reality every second of everyday and the positive reframe my light is to inform and affect society with my different lenses.

Dear Loved Soul:

I Love who I am Becoming. I grant permission to the being of human form to rebuild a solid unshort-cut process. I am safe to Play me. I am safe to Discover what canvas art gets to look like NOW! When I forget, lean on Tribe. Glance at my faults, because they are my greatest assets. Know that when darkness seeps in my thoughts: I am FIERCE WARRIOR, I am NOT ALONE, I am LOVED and CELEBRATED! My process to coming into my LIGHT is being honored. Keep moving Forward one step at a time.

I Love my passionate-Self. Burn on!

Open into your FULL wing span. Speak my TRUTH. Create through FEAR and find my LIGHT through MESS.

Love,
Re-Kindled Life

~KAR **RANTAMAKI**

My Dearest Self,

I am writing this to express my deep and unconditional love for you. I wish it was less weird and more natural for me but it seems I had to go through some s*it first in order to learn how to love you properly. First, please know that I'm sorry for the times I've forgotten who you are and what is truly important, you know, the times I sold you out. I regret any and all the times I let fear keep you stuck or allow worries of what other people think to be a factor in decisions. Excuse me for rushing through life and being overwhelmed by it all so that I missed the beauty in it. I apologize for the times I was unkind and doubted if you were strong enough, smart enough or even good enough. And also for the times I treated you like you didn't belong and then you didn't. I didn't always know better, but now I do. As a matter of fact, perhaps I'm not that sorry about these mistakes after all, because it was through them that I hurt and then learned that you deserve better. I certainly won't pretend to have it all figured out, this loving you thing, but I do know that for the rest of my days, I am committed to learning and growing in my practice of loving you, in mind, body and spirit. You, my dear self, deserve nothing less than that. You are magnificent and imperfectly perfect being and I love you. I honor you for the unique gifts you bring into the world. And so it is. Just do your thing.

Yours truly,
Nichole

~NICHOLE **WEBB**

My Body:

I'm sorry for the years of torture and hatred and hurtful words. I can't take back the years I took you for granted, but I can love you and nourish you from this moment forward. We are healing. We are rebuilding. We are in harmony-finally.

I want to thank you for all that you are. Thank you for being beautiful, inside and out. Thank you for enduring each time I put poison in you in attempts to escape. Thank you for mending each time I cut and burned you. Thank you for surviving when I starved and deprived you. Thank you for never believing that your worth was measured by the numbers on a scale, no matter how many times I tried to beat that into you. Thank you for pressing on in spite of the harsh negative words I spoke to you. Thank you for persevering when I placed you in situations that violated you. Thank you for remaining intact even after I sold you off piece by piece. I thank you for continuing the fight every time I tried to throw in the towel. I am grateful you carried us when I had given up. Thank you for creating life- twice! Most importantly, I thank you for forgiving and for healing. You are beautiful and wondrous and powerful. You are enough, you always have been. I praise, appreciate, and respect every inch of you. You are a temple; a temple of love, light, healing, and hope and I thank you for holding on long enough for me to see that.

Love,
ME

~CHRISTINA **DINE**

Photograph of Christina Dine by ~ BRANDY **LLEWELYN**

A LOVE LETTER TO MYSELF EXAMPLE—VISUAL MODIFICATIONS

~ IRENE **RODRIGUEZ**

PRACTICE SIX

MANDALA MAKING–CIRCLE OF WHOLENESS

Mandala is the Sanskrit word for circle. You may have seen intricate and very ornate designs created by monks. In many global religions and other secular traditions, the circle signifies wholeness. This practice invites you to create your own *mandala* that reflects the journey toward wholeness and integration that you've been on during this work. There is no pressure at all for your *mandala* to be ornate or intricate. This practice simply invites you to use the power container of a circle to remind you of what you have learned and teach you what you need to remember.

- Find or create a circle that you can use for this practice. A simple white paper plate is one of my favorite implements for *mandala* making. You can cut out a circle from construction or other paper. Look around your living space and you may find something completely different in the shape of a circle that is useful for the practice.
- What you put inside of the *mandala* is your decision. You can use only images, only words, or a combination. All art forms are welcome in the circle. You may even find some way to work in the Love Letter to Yourself composed in the previous practice.

- When complete, place the *mandala* somewhere you can access it easily, to be reminded of your growth. If you wish, you can bless or send an intention that your mandala represents your commitment to take care of and nourish yourself as a way of life.

MODIFICATION NOTE:

✓ If another shape represents wholeness or completeness to you better than the circle does, feel free to use it. I've seen people do this practice beautifully by intoning the shape of the heart as the container.

MANDALA MAKING EXAMPLES

~ MELITA TRAVIS **JOHNSON**

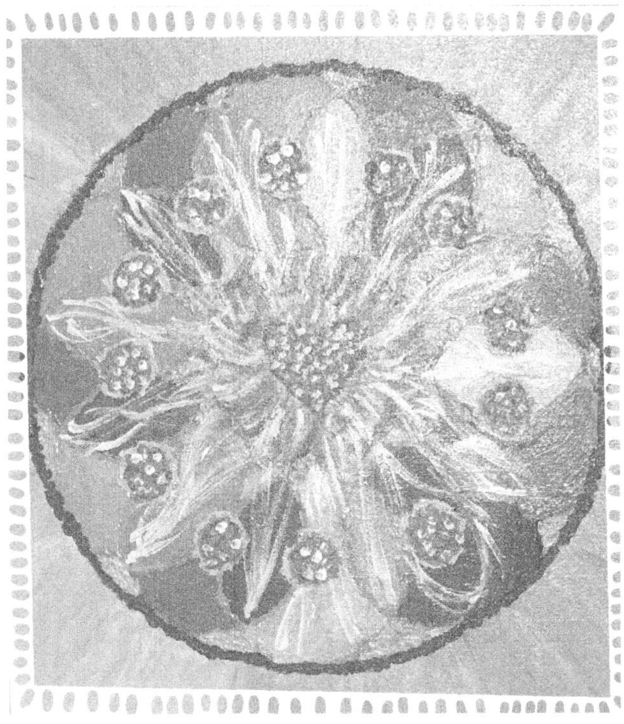

~ DR. JAMIE (PRAGYA) **MARICH**

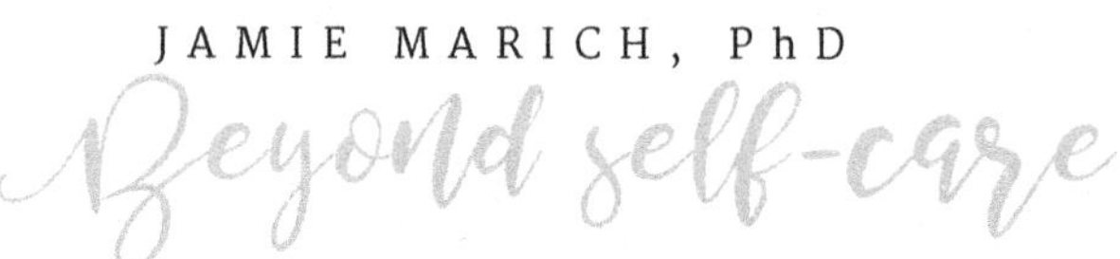

REFLECTION QUESTIONS FOLLOWING BEYOND SELF-CARE

- Describe your personal experience with the process.

- What did you discover in your process?

- What did you learn about yourself in the process?

- What did you notice about judgment or self-criticism during the process?

- What role did the multi-modality of the art forms play in discovering what you discovered in your process?

- Which of the skills explored in this process can be applied to your overall trauma recovery or wellness plan?

Process fifteen

CLAIMING THE CREATIVE VOICE

In the introduction to this book, I discussed why many of my students and clients prefer the term *expressive* to *creative.* Often, the word creative can be a hang up for us, especially if we feel that to be creative, we must be original. While most of us agree that we have something to express, relatively few of us would truly describe ourselves as creative.

Has that changed for you as a result of working the processes in this book?

Here we are—at our last formal process in this journey together. My intention in this process is to help you notice if the extent to which you identify yourself as an expressive, creative being has changed as a result of your hard work and healing. Although this book is drawing to a close, my hope is that your desire to approach life through the lens of expressive and creative processes is only just beginning!

So, I'll put the questions out there, more directly this time: What does it mean to you to be creative? And would you describe yourself as a creative person?

While I hope that your immediate, gut-level answer is *YES!*, there may still be some hesitance around claiming the word creative as a descriptor for yourself and your process. Instead of turning to the dictionary for a definition on this one, I intone one of my favorite creatives ever, writer and director Joss Whedon. Now a popular Internet meme, Whedon offers us this challenge: "Write it. Shoot it. Publish it. Crochet it. Sauté it. Whatever. MAKE."

For me, creativity is about making—literally harnessing our internal, divine birthright to bring something into existence that wasn't there before. By engaging in the practicing of making with regularity, we learn richly embodied lessons about the power of transformation and manifestation. Sure, if you are a musician and only play cover songs, you may not feel like you are contributing anything original to the sphere of creativity around you. However, consider that your version of that song offers an ever-so-slightly new twist that has the power to shift your internal world and perhaps inspire others. When you sing "Ring of Fire," even though it's been sung a million times before by thousands of other artists, you are bringing a new energetic imprint of sound and wonder into the world. You are *making*, and this makes you a creative!

Traumatic experiences leave most of us feeling pretty destroyed. At their core, the wounds of trauma are about loss, heartache, and destruction. Whenever your body, heart, and soul can show up and bring something new and beautiful and uniquely yours into the world, you are giving birth to your own recovery.

If you have come this far on your journey of expressive arts, you are a creative. You may not believe it; please know that I do! You are a magnificent, creative force. I am smiling inside as I ponder all the pieces and creations that my readers have made while working through this book. There is so much newness and vitality in this world because of your willingness to do this work and be in process. May you continue this journey, oh beautiful creative spirit, and carry this spirit to others that you encounter along the way!

PRACTICE ONE

SLOW READING

I first read *The Delight Song of Tsoai-talee* by Native American (Kiowa) writer N. Scott Momaday when I was in the 6th grade. Struggling through the turbulence of my own childhood trauma at that time, I took comfort in his idea that who I am is so much more than saying, "I am Jamie." Although I didn't understand the full impact of his words on me at that time, I've come to realize they showed me that I belong to the whole of nature and the universe. And all of these divine delights are within me!

In this practice, I will invite you into a slow reading of this poem. My instructions reflect a modified take on the ancient practice of *Lectio Divina* (sacred reading).

- Find a quiet place where you can read the poem with your full attention. Settle in and take some deep breaths before you begin reading.
- Read the poem through once. Notice if there are any words or phrases that particularly catch your attention. Without thinking about it too deeply, notice the words or the phrases. Write them down in your journal if you are so inclined.
- Read through the poem a second time, this time much slower. Notice what happens in your body and with your breath as you read his words.
- Take a pause to breathe and notice.

- Read through the poem a third time, out loud if possible. Notice if there are any new words or phrases that resonate. Write them down in your journal if you wish.
- Read through the poem a fourth time, without any special intention or directive in mind. Just notice what you notice and then enter any reflections in your journal. You can also choose to just sit with the experience.

The Delight Song of Tsoai-talee
~N. Scott Momaday

I am a feather on the bright sky
I am the blue horse that runs in the plain
I am the fish that rolls, shining, in the water
I am the shadow that follows a child
I am the evening light, the lustre of meadows
I am an eagle playing with the wind
I am a cluster of bright beads
I am the farthest star
I am the cold of dawn
I am the roaring of the rain
I am the glitter on the crust of the snow
I am the long track of the moon in a lake
I am a flame of four colors
I am a deer standing away in the dusk
I am a field of sumac and the pomme blanche
I am an angle of geese in the winter sky
I am the hunger of a young wolf
I am the whole dream of these things

You see, I am alive, I am alive
I stand in good relation to the earth
I stand in good relation to the gods
I stand in good relation to all that is beautiful
I stand in good relation to the daughter of Tsen-tainte
You see, I am alive, I am alive

MODIFICATION NOTE:

- ✓ You can engage in this slow reading process with any other poem you find that is new to you. Be advised, however, that this next practice will build upon your slow reading from this poem.

PRACTICE TWO

WRITE YOUR OWN DELIGHT SONG

The word *delight* is generally defined as something that brings us great pleasure and enjoyment. A closer look at the etymology (Middle English) reveals that the word *delight* contains the word *light* for a reason. When we delight in something, we are relishing in its light! While we may have grown accustomed to delighting in other people, places, and things, in this practice my challenge for you is to celebrate and enjoy the power of your own, eternal light. Using Momaday's poem from Practice 1 as inspiration, I invite you to write your own Delight Song. I wrote my first one back in the 6th grade, calling it *The Delight Song of Me*. You are free to title yours whatever you wish. Know that the objective is to celebrate your own light!

- Take some time to free write. Perhaps set a timer for 5 minutes and do a word chain, starting with the word "delight" or any of the other words that popped out for you when you engaged in the slow reading in Practice 1.
- In the next phase of the practice, allow "I am" phrases to come into formation and notice what happens. I challenge you to get out of the typical words and phrases you might use to describe yourself, especially if those descriptors are packed with old, negative messages.

- Your poem can be as short or as long as you need it to be. See if you can challenge yourself to make it at least three lines.

MODIFICATION NOTE:

✓ If writing is not accessible to you, see if you can recruit a friend or trusted member of your support network to help you record your Delight Song.

DELIGHT SONG EXAMPLES

delight

i am a feather on the breath of God
Feathers come in different sizes, shapes,
colors and textures
God uses my uniqueness
to radiate the world
I AM one feather, and i delight
in the feather that i am.

i am a flute through which the
wind of the hours plays music
There are a variety of flutes on this earth:
Different tones, different timbers
God uses my sometimes klunky instrument
to play in the symphony
I AM one flute, and i delight
in the flute that i am.

i am a being through which the Divine river flows
All rivers return to the ocean,
Taking different routes to get there
God has wound my river on a
weird and wonderful path
I AM one river, and i delight
in the river that i am.

~ DR. JAMIE (PRAGYA) **MARICH**
based on lines from St. Hildegard of Bingen, Khalil Gibran,
and Rainer Maria Rilke, channeling the original inspiration of Momaday

Wild Woman

I can be too much in my muchness
I am too loud in my loudness
I have never been the wilting flower or demure dame
Not my style, not my way
Nevertheless, I AM OK
Being celebrated, embraced, supported is what I seek
You will find out quick, I am not for the weak

~ RACHEL **WEAVER**

PRACTICE THREE

PROCLAIMING YOUR *DELIGHT SONG*

Composing your personal Delight Song may have elicited some strong feelings for you. Whatever those feeling were or continue to be, I hope that you allow space to be gentle with yourself in the process. You can move on to this next practice whenever you are feeling led. I offer you several options for proclaiming your personal Delight Song in lieu of modification notes for this practice.

- **OPTION 1:** Get out a recording device and share your Delight Song, as a spoken word piece. Take a pause to breathe after you proclaim it, then be sure to listen back. Notice whatever you notice.
- **OPTION 2:** If you are feeling up to it, consider video recording your Delight Song. Adding the visual dimension may create an even more powerful experience for you and your reflection.
- **OPTION 3:** Share your Delight Song with a friend or trusted member of your support group. If you are part of a regular meditation group, Women's circle or faith sharing community, consider offering this piece in that setting. There can be great power in sharing your experience in a public forum where you feel reasonably safe and supported. If you are feeling especially led, look up a local open mic night and share it there!

- **OPTION 4:** If you are a songwriter or are in the process of playing around with this skill, consider putting your Delight Song to music!
- Whichever option you choose, take some time in your journal afterwards to either write about or engage in gush art about the experience.

PRACTICE FOUR

CREATIVE IDENTITY PLAYLIST

If you've worked through the processes of the book to this point, you've gotten pretty used to making playlists. Making playlists is one of my favorite expressive arts practices to help better illuminate my thoughts, feelings, and intentions. In this practice, you are invited to create a playlist that will help you on the journey forward.

- What have you learned so far in this process or in the journey through the whole book about what it means to be creative? Take a moment to breathe and to reflect on this question.
- Now, compose a playlist (try a minimum of 5 songs) that speaks to your newly found or fully forming identity as a creative.
- One suggestion for making the playlist—go through your existing collection of music. As you scan through the titles, listen with your body. Notice the ones that pop and shimmer for you as reflective of your creative soul, even if the songs don't seem to be directly about creativity. What songs could you see yourself dancing to? Skating to? Performing to? Consider using those!
- If you are totally stuck, go to your streaming service of YouTube and simply enter in the word *creative*. Or enter in one of the words that you noticed strongly in your slow reading of *The Delight Song of Tsoai-talee*.

When you see the songs that come back in the search, listen to them, noting the guidance of the previous suggestion.

- Keep this playlist accessible! If you ever find yourself doubting your creative prowess in the journey ahead, put on this playlist. Listen to it in your car or dance to it!

MODIFICATION NOTE:

✓ **BONUS PRACTICE:** Naturally, you are invited to take this practice further and let the playlist be the backdrop for a bonus *dancing mindfulness* practice.

PRACTICE FIVE

ALBUM ART

There are few pieces of art more powerful to me than a well-designed album cover. Whether it appears on a record, a CD, or as an online image, I am in awe of the great care and creativity that goes into beautiful cover art on any collection of music. Throughout this book, you've likely gotten to know your process, your story, and your identity very well. If all your "content" was going to be the basis for an album of music, what would the cover look like?

- Consider naming your album. What word or phrase describes what you would title your album about the process of claiming your creative voice?
- Get out a piece of paper and cut it into the form of a square, or make a square in your journal (use an old CD that you might have hanging around to help you trace).
- Let your cover art come to life!
- You can also do a second or backside to the album art. You don't have to write content for the songs or tracks (unless you are feeling inspired to take this project further . . . hint, hint). However, I challenge you to come up with 5-10 tracks or song titles that would go onto this album.

MODIFICATION NOTE:

- ✓ If the idea of a book cover works better for you than an album cover, use that. After designing a book cover about the process of claiming your creative voice, design a back cover and write a description for your book.

ALBUM ART EXAMPLES

Stairwell

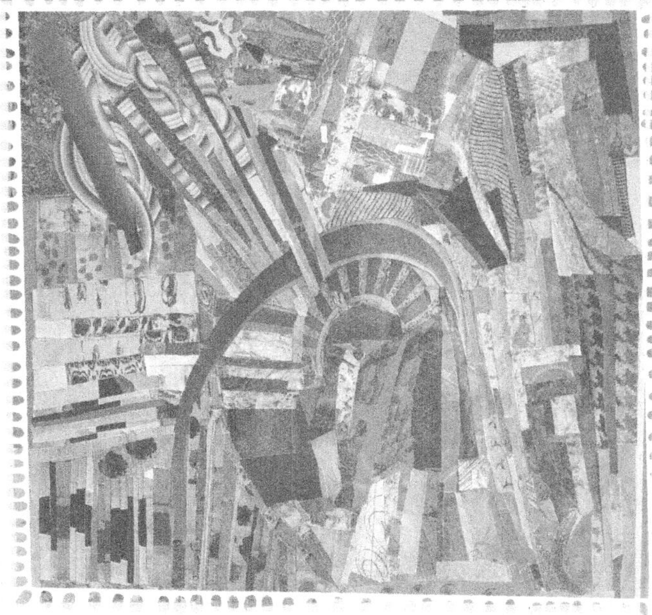

~ EDWARD **CARSON, ESQ**

~ DR. JAMIE (PRAGYA) **MARICH**
(This is the album cover from a 2012 release where I developed this practice)

PRACTICE SIX

THE CREATIVE'S MISSION STATEMENT

The concept of a mission statement may come with dry connotations. Yes, many of us have worked for companies with mission statements. We may roll our eyes even harder if the company in question has a mission statement that doesn't quite fit with the values they put into action. I believe that mission statements can be a beautiful thing—they can help us to clarify our values and intentions for our personal work in this world and set us on the healthiest possible path. Indeed, the word *mission* is Latin in its origin—it literally means, to "send off."

For this last practice, I send you on your way by challenging you to develop your own personal mission statement. In this mission statement, declare who you are as a creative and how you see yourself in the world as an expressive being. May this serve as sustenance and as a guiding light for your road ahead!

- If you need to see some samples for inspiration, go to your favorite Internet search engine and type in the phrase "Mission Statement." You won't have any trouble finding one.
- Begin crafting your own personal mission statement as a creative. Try to keep it under a page so it's something you can access quickly if you need to.

- If you need several drafts until you can come up with the wording that feels best in your body and soul, let yourself have that process. If necessary, you can even let it evolve over a few days.
- You are also free to decorate your mission statement in your journal or on the page where you created it. Use the full range of your expressive arts practices. A visual mission statement may work for you even better than a written one.
- Keep this in a place where you can access it easily and often. Consider sharing it with others who have supported you in this expressive journey of healing and transformation.

MISSION STATEMENT EXAMPLES

I am committed to promoting holistic health for myself and others through the power of the creative arts. Creativity is a divinely gifted super power that all humanity possesses. It is my mission to stay creatively alive in every aspect of my life, through every stage of my life. I call upon the gift of creativity to serve my right to express myself, my right to communicate and collaborate with others and to co-create a more socially just world through the creative arts.
I call upon the power of creativity to assist me in facing the challenges of life. It is my mission to take responsibility for my trauma recovery process and to use the power of the creative arts to serve my healing. I find the arts of expressive body movement, self-reflective writing and drawing to be extremely effective in releasing and transforming the effects of trauma from my bodymind.

My mission includes a willingness to integrate mindfulness principles into my daily life. I aspire to stay focused on the present moment, and perceive myself and others through the lens of acceptance, non-judgment, and respect for the complex challenges of the human experience.

~ JOANNA **CASHMAN**

My Personal Creative Mission is to embrace life with an open mind, learning from the world to be a better me. To maintain a lifelong commitment to learning that awakens my spiritual purpose, promoting mental resilience and well-being. To encourage, interact, engage, and equip others to believe in the possibilities on a daily basis. To positively impact the life of every person I meet on my holistic journey, through dance.

~ GEETA **PENDAER**

Through my creative process, may I
see all I need to see
hear all I need to hear
say all I need to say
touch all I need to touch
feel all I need to feel
move all I need to move
be still with everything I need to sit with
and create all I need to create.

And may I empower others to do the same

~ RAMONA **SKRIIKO**

CREATIVES' MISSION STATEMENT EXAMPLES—VISUAL MODIFICATIONS

~ KELSEY **EVANS**

~ KAMALA **TAHYI**

Inhale. Live this moment. Exhale. Live this moment. Inhale. Live this moment. Exhale. Live This Moment. Inhale. Live this moment. Exhale. Live this moment. Inhale. Live this moment. Exhale Live this moment. Inhale. Live this moment. Exhale. Live this moment. Inhale. Live this moment. Exhale. Live this moment. Inhale. Live this moment. Exhale. Live this moment. Inhale. Live this moment. Exhale. Live this moment.

~ MYRA **RUBENSTEIN**

REFLECTION QUESTIONS FOLLOWING CLAIMING THE CREATIVE VOICE

- Describe your personal experience with the process.
- What did you discover in your process?
- What did you learn about yourself in the process?
- What did you notice about judgment or self-criticism during the process?
- What role did the multi-modality of the art forms play in discovering what you discovered in your process?
- Which of the skills explored in this process can be applied to your overall trauma recovery or wellness plan?

Conclusion

THE LIFESTYLE OF RECOVERY AND THE EXPRESSIVE ARTS

The debates are intense in both addiction and mental health recovery circles about what works best for helping people heal. Having been in the field for quite some time now, I've been stuck in the crossfire of opinion and conjecture. I've mediated fights between rigid proponents of 12-step recovery and those who declare such methods to be ineffective and cultish. On the mental health side of things, similar arguments happen between proponents of methods that are more cognitive in nature versus those that are more embodied and holistic.

From my days as a graduate student, I became fascinated by what all of the approaches to recovery and healing seem to have in common. When I read Anne Fletcher's landmark book *Sober for Good* the common thread dawned on me—lifestyle change.[13] If any therapy, program, approach, method, fellowship, or self-help strategy helps you to bring about meaningful lifestyle change, you have a good chance of getting well. So what exactly does *lifestyle change* mean, and what is the role of expressive arts practices in cultivating a healthy lifestyle?

Although now a common expression used in the English language, the word lifestyle traces back to the writings of psychoanalyst Alfred Adler in the

[13] Fletcher, A. (2002). *Sober for Good: New Solutions for Drinking Problems. Advice from Those Who Succeeded.* New York: Rux Martin/Houghton Mifflin.

late 1920's. According to Adler, our lifestyle develops to help us respond to our own inadequacies. In Adlerian psychology, lifestyle is synonymous with the psyche and personality, as these lifestyle patterns tend to develop before the age of nine. Adler, who contended that lifestyle originated in childhood, described it as the pair of eyeglasses through which every individual sees their world. Carrying this metaphor a step further, to bring about change in those aspects of lifestyle that cause problems for an individual requires a new pair of glasses—or at least an adjustment on the existing prescription. A major mechanism of change in Adlerian Psychology is recognizing that one's inferiority can inspire them to "movement and action." To bring about this change, one must have a clear goal or vision for how they would like to manifest change in their style of living.[14]

Expressive arts challenge us to take action and to move toward our higher and healthiest sense of self.

Process Not Perfection offers you ample opportunities to get to know yourself more fully. If you have read the book and gone through its processes and practices, I applaud you for accepting the invitations to journey deeper into your own healing. The greatest gift I've ever received is the gift of transformation through lifestyle change, and I am grateful every day for the role that expressive arts has played, and continues to play in this process.

To fully unwrap the gift of self-discovery I hope you have received by working through this book, I invite you into one more concluding practice. Inspired by the Adlerian metaphor of the new pair of glasses, I also hope that this concluding practice will give you a final fine tuning before you venture out into your life beyond these pages. Onward!

---

[14] Adler, A. (1929). *The Science of Living.* New York: Garden City Publishing Company; pp. 98-100.

CONCLUDING PRACTICE: BEFORE AND AFTER VIEWS

Staying with Adler's metaphor of the glasses, in this concluding practice, I invite you to develop "before" and "after" images that represent the vision of life that you saw through your lifestyle glasses before your work in this book and after engaging in the work of this book.

Many art forms can be included here. You can work an old pair of glasses into your visual art, or consider taking two plain paper plates and allow one to represent the "before" and one to represent the "after." Drawing, collage, or even "before and after" playlists are all viable options.

Once you've engaged in this concluding practice, take some time to reflect, either in silent meditation or in writing. By working directly with your "before and after" prescriptions, what lessons can you glean about the best possible lifestyle choices you can make for yourself going forward? What may be standing in the way of making these bold choices in the service of your recovery and wellness?

My hope is that through the processes in this book and your experience so far with the expressive arts, you have embraced both movement and action. Up until this point, your struggles with trauma and/or addiction may have led you to develop lifestyle patterns that helped you cope temporarily, but ultimately left you stuck inside. Expressive arts challenge us to take action and to move toward our higher and healthiest sense of self.

I trust that you have learned some vital lessons about how you can change your overall lifestyle through the power of process. In her memoir *Tango Lessons*, young writer Meghan Flaherty declares "Tango is something that you are. Not something you do."[15] You can fill in the blank: Where she uses the word *tango* based on her transformational experience with that art, what can

[15] Flaherty, M. (2018). *Tango Lessons*. New York: Houghton Mifflin, p. 246.

you use? Maybe it's the entire buffet of expressive arts that you've come to know in your work through this book. Perhaps it's one or two specific practices that have come to define your joy and your passion.

Find that practice or those practices that extract the juice from your soul—the practices that transform how you respond to your old pre-programmed messages about yourself that keep you stuck in those loops of inferiority and self-doubt. Once you've made that discovery your entire lifestyle has the potential to be transformed, and your growth toward health and wholeness is unchained and unlimited. You may be well on that road or still in need of some discovery. Wherever you are at today, I honor that.

There are many more expressive practices that are not specifically covered in this book. The practices I elected to include are those that can generally be followed through reading instructions in the context of a book, with a bare minimum of materials and training. Other practices that may appeal to you, especially if you are feeling adventurous, include:

- Body painting or working with body markers (washable)
- Clay and sculpting
- Gardening
- Quilting
- Short film and filmmaking
- Tattoo design
- Songwriting
- Martial arts
- Clothing design
- Hair and make-up design

If you have training in any of these specific practices, think of how you might be able to take any of the processes in this book and apply one or more of the practices to deepen into the theme of that process.

You may also notice that, in reading over this list, one of the practices I mentioned really shimmers or pops for you. For instance, if you've always wanted to work with clay, consider going to your local craft store and getting some, just to experiment. Explore where you may be able to find a class in your local community. All of these practices can be studied and pursuing those that interest you may be a vital component in helping you to shift how you spend your time and energy as a person with a set intention for recovery and a deeper sense of healing.

Although the martial arts intrigued me over the years, I never saw myself as a person who would actually begin studying them, especially with the messages of inferiority about not being a good enough athlete that I carried around. Through learning to live a life in process over my years in recovery and the expressive arts, in early 2017 I finally responded to the invitation to attend a class with a coach who had a good reputation for being accessible and trauma-informed. Now, I cannot image my life without the two main practices that I've learned—Brazilian/Gracie Jiu-Jitsu and kickboxing—from Micah, my wise guide.

Now that you've taken your exploratory dive into the expressive arts, finding your own wise guide may be a next step on your journey. Sponsorship is promoted within 12-step recovery circles, and working with a teacher is encouraged in many Eastern meditation traditions. Similarly, having an expressive arts teacher or facilitator that you can study with personally may help you deepen your connection to your practices of choice, or to the overall experience of living your life as an expressive artist. Your guide may come in the form of a teacher or a friend/member of your support system who is committed to a lifestyle of wellness and healing that includes the expressive arts.

Working through the entirety *of Process Not Perfection* is a major undertaking, and I personally salute you for your willingness to be daring and bold and expressive! I hope that your journey will not end here. My wish for you is that what you have learned in this book about your power to express and to create will inspire you to make expressive arts a vital part of your lifestyle. Living your life in process opens you up to vast resources and connections and allows you to see the possibilities in every challenge that life may put in your path. May the fruits (and juices) of your practice continue to nourish you in this quest!

Appendix

ADDITIONAL RESOURCES

FEATURED WEBSITE:

www.traumamadesimple.com/pnp

Visit Dr. Jamie Marich's resources site *Trauma Made Simple* to access this special page set up to accompany *Process Not Perfection*. On this site you can view the artwork from the book in full color, and have easy access to video demonstrations of the meditation and movement exercises presented.

The main website, *Trauma Made Simple*, also leads you to everything complementary that Dr. Jamie offers on trauma recovery and wellness online. There are plenty of articles and videos (including her well-received TEDx talk on trauma from 2015) that you can access for your personal study.

ONLINE COMMUNITY:

DANCING MINDFULNESS & EXPRESSIVE ARTS COMMUNITY FORUM

www.facebook.com/groups/DancingMindfulnessCommunity/

An online forum designed for those wanting to connect with others who are engaged in expressive arts work with Dr. Jamie Marich. Initially set up for the release of *Dancing Mindfulness: A Creative Path to Healing and Transformation* in 2015, this forum has continued to grow. Feel free to ask questions, connect with others, or to share the fruits of your processes!

DANCING MINDFULNESS EXPRESSIVE ARTS BLOG

www.dancingmindfulness.com/expressive-arts-blog

The official expressive arts blog of the *Dancing Mindfulness* community, curated by Dr. Jamie Marich. Although a major outlet for Dr. Jamie's original work, submissions from the community are always welcome. This is an excellent way to share pieces from your work through *Process Not Perfection*.

OTHER FAVORITE WEBSITES FROM DR. JAMIE MARICH

Visit the websites and online resources connected to the work of Dr. Jamie's teachers and other sources of inspiration presented in the book:

- Abbey of the Arts (the work of Dr. Christine Valters Paintner)
  www.abbeyofthearts.com
- Carl Rogers and Natalie Rogers (the official website of Natalie Rogers)
  www.nrogers.com
- Angeles Arrien: Walking the Mystical Path with Practical Feet
  www.angelesarrien.com
- The International Expressive Arts Therapy Association (IEATA)
  www.ieata.org
- Amrit Yoga Institute
  www.amrityoga.org
  *You can also search Amrit Yoga Institute on YouTube for a wide complementary collection of yoga nidra meditations
- Krishna Das Music
  www.krishnadasmusic.com
  *You can also search for Krishna Das on Apple Music and Spotify, where he makes dozens of his own workshops on practice and process available.

Made in the USA
Las Vegas, NV
26 February 2022

44657623R00223